About the Author

Daniel Piper is a poet and comedian.

He has been seen and heard on national TV and radio and has performed across Europe and the UK at festivals including Latitude, Bestival and Edinburgh International Book Festival. He has written and performed two smash-hit Edinburgh shows – 'Daniel Piper is in Four Gangs' (2016) and 'Daniel Piper's Day Off' (2017).

Daniel is the 2017 Scottish National Poetry Slam champion. In May the same year, he came second in the world championships in Paris (first the worst, second the best, etc). He has written for publications including *The Skinny* and *The Alarmist*, and in 2018 his Instagram writing page (@danielpiperwords) was named a 'must-follow account' by *Wallpaper* magazine.

To Amy,

Thanks for buying my book!! :)

D0531624

~~IRRESPONSIBLE AND NONESSENTIAL~~
~~UNREASONABLE AND IMPERTINENT~~
~~DIRECTIONLESS AND EXPENDABLE~~
~~INCONSISTENT AND REDUNDANT~~
~~UNSCIENTIFIC AND EXORBITANT~~
ARBITRARY AND UNNECESSARY
~~IRRATIONAL AND SUPERFLUOUS~~
~~CROTCHETY AND UNREQUIRED~~
~~CONTRARY AND UNDESIRABLE~~
~~DESULTORY AND HAPHAZARD~~
~~WAYWARD AND EXTRANEOUS~~
~~SUBJECTIVE AND PERIPHERAL~~
~~SUPERFICIAL AND CAUSELESS~~
~~ABERRANT AND REDUNDANT~~
~~IRREGULAR AND DISPOSABLE~~
~~INCONSTANT AND NEEDLESS~~
~~FLIGHTY AND THOUGHTLESS~~
~~FRIVOLOUS AND IRRELEVANT~~
~~INJUDICIOUS AND USELESS~~
~~FLUCTUANT AND EXTRINSIC~~
~~ERRATIC AND GRATUITOUS~~
~~CAPRICIOUS AND FUTILE~~
~~VAGARIOUS AND TRIVIAL~~
~~DICEY AND SURPLUS~~
~~FLAKY AND VAGRANT~~
~~FITFUL AND WANTON~~

ARBITRARY & UNNECESSARY

ARBITRARY & UNNECESSARY

THE SELECTED WORKS OF DANIEL PIPER (SELECTED BY DANIEL PIPER)

DANIEL PIPER

Unbound Digital

This edition first published in 2018

Unbound

6th Floor Mutual House, 70 Conduit Street, London W1S 2GF

www.unbound.com

ISBN (eBook): 978-1-912618-91-0
ISBN (Paperback): 978-1-912618-90-3

Cover design by Mecob
Cover photograph © Perry Jonsson

Printed and bound in Great Britain by Clays Ltd, Elcograf S.p.A.

Author's note

This book was made possible by a successful crowdfunding campaign. While it was always going to be dedicated to my girlfriend, a second dedication was available as a reward for one of the higher pledge levels. Either that pledger has a very unusual name, or they pledged under the name of a business.

For Jemima
&
Jolly Nice Farmshop

Dear Reader,

The book you are holding came about in a rather different way to most others. It was funded directly by readers through a new website: Unbound.

Unbound is the creation of three writers. We started the company because we believed there had to be a better deal for both writers and readers. On the Unbound website, authors share the ideas for the books they want to write directly with readers. If enough of you support the book by pledging for it in advance, we produce a beautifully bound special subscribers' edition and distribute a regular edition and e-book wherever books are sold, in shops and online.

This new way of publishing is actually a very old idea (Samuel Johnson funded his dictionary this way). We're just using the internet to build each writer a network of patrons. Here, at the back of this book, you'll find the names of all the people who made it happen.

Publishing in this way means readers are no longer just passive consumers of the books they buy, and authors are free to write the books they really want. They get a much fairer return too – half the profits their books generate, rather than a tiny percentage of the cover price.

If you're not yet a subscriber, we hope that you'll want to join our publishing revolution and have your name listed in one of our books in the future. To get you started, here is a £5 discount on your first pledge. Just visit unbound.com, make your pledge and type DANIEL18 in the promo code box when you check out.

Thank you for your support,

Dan, Justin and John
Founders, Unbound

Super Patrons

Mark Adams
Bert Aerts
Darran Arnell
Mick Barry
Ariguun Batkhishig
Sara Bennison
Lucy Brown
Francesca Cole
Gavin Collins
John Corbett
Beverley Cowen
Ellie Dawes
Aisling Doonan
William Eaves
Alexandra Ehrlich Speiser
Liam 'Twinkle Toes' Fleming
Kriss Foster
Cathy Gallagher
James Hayle
Helen Hegarty
Sean Hickman
Pete and Kath Hickman
Thom Hoffman
Benji Huntrods
Tom Jobling
Alex Jones
Dan Kieran
Nikki Lee
Sarah Lippett
Nicki Marsh
Hannah Mary
Josie McGregor

John Mitchinson
Anand Modha
Kimberley Montgomery
Simon Moriarty
Heather Moulson
Thomas Muirhead
Claire Mullord
Colin Nelson
Bernard and Jane Nelson
Anthony Newton
Jolly Nice
Karen Nicholson
Rhymes with Orange
Jane Overton
Dan Parkes
@photoldories
Alison Piper
Mike Piper
Justin Pollard
David Pursglove
Chris Read
Martha Robinson
Lozza Robs
Sophie Rowe
@samschulzstudio
David Sanders
Emily & Bill Sanderson
Will Sanderson-Thwaite
Reuben Scott
Rodger Smith
Ashley Sykes
Cecilia Tetbury
Stevie Tyler
Ian Wakefield
Simon Weekes
Jemima Wilson

Sam Wong
Tymek Woodham

Foreword

Daniel Piper was one of the great literary bohemians of the late noughties and early teenies. He was a dandy and a raconteur who held court in the drinking dens of Fitzrovia. Vivid, louche and slangy, his writing conjures up a smoky world of Ubers and flat whites.

Piper was a prolific novelist, poet and social media user. For much of his young adult life he lived a perilous existence, continually short of money and harassed by creditors, landlords and EE. Indeed, to read any of Piper's novels is to be plunged into a world whose boundaries consisted only of the saloon bar and the seedy love nest in Peckham where he conducted a dangerous and secret affair with his long-term girlfriend.

Piper remains an elusive, if not a vagrant figure. He was born in 1991 in Chesterfield. From the ages of three to five he attended Cherry Burton preschool. Even at this young age, Piper's signature interrogation of the human condition was already manifesting (as evidenced by found VHS footage of his searching portrayal of Joseph in the preschool nativity). He subsequently attended Cherry Burton Primary School, followed by Beverley Grammar School. Sadly, little is known of his time at either institution, although one recovered report from the latter describes 'a fierce intelligence akin to Stephens both Fry and Hawking (alongside the warmth of Les Dennis)'.

After completing his A-Levels, Piper studied Literature and Creative Writing at the University of Warwick, where he discovered a natural flair for being an absolutely brilliant writer. After graduating, he decided – somewhat unconventionally – to set off for London.

During the early teenies, it would have been impossible to enter any drinking den in the capital without encountering painters, poets, anarchists and literary drunks, hard at work on their memoirs, poetry collections, blogs and vlogs. But even among this collection of bohemians, Piper is said to have cast his own distinctive shadow – particularly in his dandyish get-up of white T-shirt, jeans and brogues.

Piper's first and only novel was published in 2019. Even its title,

Again and Not Again, demonstrates a flagrant disregard for convention. By taking the well-known phrase *again and again* and simply adding the word *not*, he changes the meaning completely and gives birth to a quintessential example of Piperian wordplay.

Piper's strength as a novelist derives from his telegraphic but curiously weighted prose style. Take, for example, the following passage, which introduces the reader to *Again and Not Again*'s suave and debonair protagonist, Paniel Diper:

Paniel entered the cafe, causing female heads to turn in his direction because of his good-looking face. He walked deliberately (like a panther). As he approached the counter, he took his vape from his pocket and inhaled gorgeously.

'Flat white, please,' he said in a deep voice with a hint of vulnerability because of a past trauma.

'Coming right up,' said the barista, turning away.

'Wait,' said Paniel. 'What's the Wi-Fi code here?'

'It's espresso,' she replied. Paniel leaned forward onto the counter. 'All lowercase?' he whispered. The barista was visibly aroused.

'Yes,' she said, audibly aroused.

'Thanks,' said Paniel, blowing vape smoke into her face and arousing her even more (visibly and audibly).

Again and Not Again was Piper's greatest achievement. The path thereafter led downwards. His second novel, *Over and Not Over*, was a critical and commercial failure. Increasingly crippled with debt in London, Piper moved to the Netherlands, where he is believed to have settled into a quiet life as a freelance windmill operator. His fans still live in hope that he will return to England and publish new work. This is, of course, unlikely. Piper is long presumed dead, rumoured to have cycled into a canal after suffering a cannabis-induced hallucination inside the Amsterdam Madame Tussauds, and believing that he was being pursued by a waxwork of Kylie Minogue.

All scholars will agree that the Dutch canal's gain was the literary world's loss. All we can do now is savour and enjoy this recently dis-covered collection of Piper's early writing again and again. Tragically for us, Piper's literary career was a case of again and not again.

Anonymous, July 2018, Amsterdam

Living

I decided, after reading a motivational poster, to start living each day like it was my last. Today was day one. I woke up early, called my parents and told them the sad news. They were devastated. After sending a group text to some close friends, I began sorting my affairs: writing my will, cancelling contracts and bequeathing my social media accounts to a responsible heir. When I was finally ready to leave the house, it was dark outside, so I stayed in and watched videos of other people skydiving. If I'm honest, it hasn't been that great a day and I'm not hugely excited about doing it all again tomorrow.

The Metamorphillip

It had been a long time since Phillip Schofield had last looked into the mirror. He had been very busy with *This Morning* and it wasn't until he did look into the mirror one Tuesday morning that he realised he was no longer Phillip Schofield the man. At some point between now and the last time he had looked into the mirror (at least two months ago), he had become Phillip Schofield the fish. At first he was surprised. *Why had nobody told me?* he thought. Then he looked at his watch. Five-thirty! He had to be at the ITV studios in less than half an hour.

[I haven't written the middle of this story. I'm thinking that Phillip goes to work, people realise he's a fish and there are all sorts of high jinks. I have written the end though. All you need to know is that Phillip is now in a restaurant and at some point during the day he has changed his name to Fiship Scalefield.]

The waiter approached. Are you ready to order, Mr Scalefield?

Fiship looked at the menu. Hmm. I'm not sure. Do you recommend anything?

Let me see, said the waiter. The fish is good.

Fiship laughed. No, thanks! he said. I think I've had enough fish for one day! I am one.

How to Cheat on Your Partner When Your Partner is Away in Germany

- Organise a party, inviting nine people with whom you would like to conduct the infidelity.
- During the party, conduct the infidelity with those nine people.
- When your partner returns from Germany and asks whether you were unfaithful, simply reply: *Nine*.

Comedy

When the taxi driver heard that I dabbled in comedy, he told me to tell him a joke. I explained that I didn't really do jokes, more like storytelling or poetry to be honest. He asked if I wanted to hear a joke about his penis but then said, never mind actually, it's too long. It was a shame because I did want to hear it.

The Wrong Side of Twenty-Five

I'm on the wrong side of twenty-five
but the right side of thirty.
I'm on the right side of twenty-seven
but the wrong side of thirteen

because I'm twice that now, I'm twenty-six
and that's halfway to a full deck.
In a few years, I'll be fifty-two
and in a few more, I'll be dead.

I'm old, I'm twenty-six,
my railcard days are numbered.
If I want to spend Christmas at home this year
it'll have to be crowdfunded.

I'm old, I'm boring,
I've started drinking tea.
Instead of going out, I stay in
and shout at my TV.

If I went on *The X Factor*,
I'd be in the Overs category.
I'd be the old bloke they let on as a joke
so the audience can laugh at me.

I'm old, I'm washed up,
my glory days are ending.
And I know what you're thinking
if you're older than me,
you're thinking, Stop pretending.

You're not old, you ungrateful shit,
you've still got your life ahead of you.
I'd give anything to go back in time
and be twenty-six instead of you.

But haven't you noticed? Things have changed,
have you been on YouTube recently?
There are millionaires on there
who retire at twenty-three.
Beyoncé's newborn babies have got more
Twitter followers than me.

I'm old, I'm twenty-six,
I've started reminiscing.
I've started ranting and raving
to anybody who will listen.

About the never-ending party
that was mid-to-late noughties;
Skins, Popworld, Hollyoaks,
early Arctic Monkeys.
Kids these days listen to vinyl
but we made do with iPods,
and if you had a Motorola Razr,
you were automatically a heart-throb
(and I had one).

If you wanted to make friends in my day,
you had to *talk* to people
(on MySpace).

I'm old, I'm washed up,
the party's truly over.

Yesterday I bought myself
a sleeveless knitted jumper.

I got myself a flat cap
and a bottle of Brut Cologne.
Tomorrow morning, I'm packing my bags
and checking into a home.

Muscle

In an attempt to become more attractive, I decided to work on my muscles. It would also be a chance to assert my individuality; there are over six hundred muscles in the human body, so why go for something obvious like the arms or chest? In the end, I decided to develop my occipitofrontalis muscle (in front of the forehead). Every day for six months, I raised my eyebrows three hundred times (five sets of sixty reps). Tonight I am going to a nightclub, where I will debut my new hench forehead. I can't wait.

an influencer
caught influenza
it went viral
everyone died

Beautiful

It struck me while listening to One Direction's 'What Makes You Beautiful' that the girl in question would cease to be beautiful if she heard the song, since not knowing her beauty was what made her beautiful. Desperate to warn her, I tracked her down to a hut near the beach from the video. She answered the door with a bag over her head. I was her first visitor in years. She had heard the song on its release and transformed immediately. The only thing keeping her going now was the hope that the boys might one day reform and write a new song in which she was beautiful, even though she knew it.

TG

It was Friday, so I decided to try visiting TGI Fridays. Upon arrival, I asked what time the service would begin. The waitress was confused. I explained that I assumed they gave thanks on a Friday (since the name is short for Thank God It's Friday). She told me this wasn't the case, but I was welcome to stay for a burger. I was quite disappointed; I had chosen this particular TGI Fridays after reading online that the service was excellent.

Previously

Worried that my life had become boring, I hired an actor to follow me around all day and wake me every morning by shouting *Previously!* and then acting out a montage of key scenes from the day before. He dramatised scenes of me catching the train to work or sending and receiving emails, and even managed to end every recap with a cliff-hanger: *Could* I attend next week's sales meeting? *Would* I maybe like to go for a drink with Jane? *Was* it a sackable offence to bring an actor to the sales meeting? I don't leave the house much these days but, with Gary here, it's never boring.

Mosquito

I received a mosquito bite to the face. I was quite annoyed; they usually avoided the face and it felt as though a silent agreement had been broken. The next evening, I wrote a letter of complaint and left it by my bedroom window. I awoke to a handwritten apology by the head mosquito, informing me that a member of her team had indeed breached the code of conduct and had been reprimanded. She also told me that her entire unit would be receiving mandatory bite training to ensure that they targeted only the body in future. I was satisfied with her response and decided not to take the matter any further.

your love
was like a portable charger
for the battery
of my heart

but then the portable charger ran out of charge
so we got another portable charger
(to charge the first portable charger)
but then that portable charger ran out of charge
and the shop had no more portable chargers

(this metaphor isn't working
basically, we fell out of love)

Arm

My arm had to be amputated after I slept on it wrong. To avoid humiliation, I said that I had lost it during an altercation with a bear. I became famous within the survivalism community and was invited to appear at several conferences around the world. My fraudulence was exposed live on Australian radio when I was unable to instruct a caller on how to skin an alligator. All subsequent conference appearances were cancelled and I was dropped as the face of Altitude Knives.

Friends

In an attempt to find out who my real friends were, I brought my birthday forward by one day on Facebook. I received several messages and soon forgot about my experiment, instead allowing myself to simply delight in hearing from old friends and faraway relatives, especially those suggesting we reconnect and meet up soon. The next day, joy turned to despair when I received no Facebook messages and one email, along with the dawning realisation that my only real friend is easyJet.

Survival

My survival started on the day that I was born,
you see, I was born five weeks premature.
All the other mothers who were on the ward
were told to come and look at me
because I was so small.

I was tiny, like a baby,
but like a really, really, really small baby.
So small that my Mum had to dress me
in dolls' clothes.[1]
But I survived.

My first day at school, it wasn't very fun.
I asked Mrs Dixon to wipe my bum.
I thought it was normal.
But it's not.

Year 2 PE, in the school hall,
Mrs Manning lined us all up against the wall.
She said, *I want to see you all do a forward roll,*
But I couldn't do forward rolls.

I said I couldn't do it but she wasn't having that.
When it got to my turn, she made me walk up to the mat.
I gave it a go and on my face, I fell flat
—they all laughed
But I survived.

1. Specifically Tiny Tears.

Scars on my body.
Scars on my brain.
Those ones are emotional,
but they cause the most pain.

I was very upset when I started big school,
all the other boys were into football.
I pretended I was too, to try and seem cool
but when asked who my favourite player was, I said Tim Henman.

I got my first girlfriend in Year 8.
Met her on MSN, asked her out on a date.
We went to the cinema to see *The Day After Tomorrow*
and then the day after that, I got dumped.

I had my first fight with a boy called Sam Ford.
He pushed me really hard into an interactive whiteboard.
It messed with the projection, it wouldn't turn on,
then I got detention
—it wasn't my fault!

Scars on my body.
Scars on my brain.
Those ones are emotional,
but they cause the most pain.

I went to Morocco, had a traditional massage,
I thought it'd be relaxing but it was actually really harsh.
The masseuse's glove was practically made of Velcro
—it made me cry.

I went to Barcelona and was swimming in the sea
when a bloody jellyfish went and stung me.
I ran into a bar, asked the barman what to do
and he pointed at my arm, said,
You know what to do.

So I ran into the toilet and pissed all over my arm.
I really soiled it. I tried to stay calm.
Then when I left the toilet there were more barmen, all standing and
laughing at me, and one of them said,
You could have used vinegar.

And if I'm brave enough to ever read this poem live,
I hope I do it justice and I make people cry,
make them think, *Fair enough, he's had a bad time.*
Because I've seen a lot of trouble and I've seen a lot of strife
(And I don't just mean the cockney rhyming slang for wife),
I mean I've been through a lot of struggle in my life,
but I get knocked down,
I get up again,
I stand up tall
(5'8" [and a half])
and I survive.

(This piece is dedicated to my mum.)

Playlist

I heard a song I liked on Spotify and was about to add it to a playlist when I realised I couldn't decide which one. It was slightly too chilled for Party and slightly too party-ish for Chill. After some back and forth, I added it to Party. A few nights later, it was my girlfriend's birthday party. Our flat was heaving, my Party playlist was shuffled on full blast and everyone was dancing and having a great time until that song came on. It was just too chilled. The mood never quite recovered.

Ring

After weeks of deliberation, I decided that Valentine's was the perfect day to finally give my beloved a ring. I practised my words several times in front of the mirror and ironed my best shirt in preparation for the moment. As the sun began to set and the stars started shining iridescent across the evening sky, I took a deep breath and reached into my pocket. It rang twice before she cancelled the call.

A Short Play about Tina and Her Silly Husband Barry

[TINA and her silly husband BARRY are waiting for a train. It is late]

TINA: How do you find out if a train is delayed?

BARRY: I don't know, how *do* you find out if a train is delayed?

TINA: No, Barry, It wasn't a joke. It was a question. There's nothing on the timetable screen, so how do you find out if a train is delayed?

BARRY: I don't know, how *do* you find out if a train is delayed?

TINA: Oh never mind.

BARRY: I don't get it.

[Curtain]

Poetry

She asked if I read poetry and I said yes. It wasn't a huge lie – I had been meaning to start reading poetry and I wanted to appear cultured on our first date. It was perhaps unwise to add that I also wrote poems (specifically love poems) but the food thankfully arrived a moment later. After dinner, during a moonlit stroll, she suddenly asked to hear one of my love poems. Panicking, I searched for something, anything, then remembered a poem from school. I looked into her eyes and whispered profoundly, Divorced, beheaded, died. Divorced, beheaded, survived. We did not meet again.

after you kissed me
i told you i was the luckiest man alive

but then i read about a man who became a millionaire after accidentally buying an original copy of the declaration of independence at a flea market

so i took it back

A More Accurate but Less Aurally Satisfying Version of the Rhyme about Henry VIII's Six Wives

Divorced, beheaded, died.
Divorced, beheaded, outlived Henry.

Chat

She invited me to the office not for an interview but for a chat, so I spent all week researching the kind of things I like to chat about. I don't think I've got the job. She kept asking what I could bring to the team and I kept talking about how underwhelmed I was by *Spectre*, particularly after *Skyfall*.

Information

I read an interview in which Ed Sheeran revealed that he does not own a mobile phone. Although I thought little of it at the time, the information slowly began to affect my daily life. I couldn't look at my own phone without thinking Ed Sheeran doesn't have one of these. I couldn't make a call without thinking Ed Sheeran can't do this. I knew something was wrong with me when the 'Beast from the East' brought heavy snowfall to the UK. While everybody else was complaining about disrupted travel, all I could think about was whether anybody had checked on Ed Sheeran.

Ian

Ian was bored at home so he called up his mother-in-law and ate crisps down the phone. She thought there was a network problem so she called back a few minutes later.

Sorry, Ian, I think there was a network problem before. Did you need something?
   No. I was bored, so I called you up and ate crisps down the phone.
   Oh, right. Well, I'll speak to you soon. Bye, Ian.
   —Hang on a minute…

Ian placed another handful of crisps into his mouth and ate them loudly down the phone.

Interview

I've got a job interview tomorrow, so I'm looking for my interviewers on Facebook. They're probably doing the same to me. Sniffing me out. Seeing if I like a drink. I can only find Sarah Jones. Mike King doesn't seem to have an account. Sarah looks fun. I can see that she has lots of friends, and she likes a drink. It looks like she had a laugh in Kavos last summer. And in All Bar One last week. I think we'd get on, Sarah and I. We'd be good friends. Which means we'd work well together.

Friend request sent.

Now that we're friends, there'll be great chemistry in tomorrow's interview. Mike will feel left out. He won't understand the private jokes. He'll keep trying to edge into the conversation and steer it back to the questions.

Humour

A few hours into my first day in the office, my boss summoned us to watch a funny YouTube video over her shoulder. Keen to demonstrate a good sense of humour in front of my new team, I began laughing heartily as soon as the video began. The others remained silent until, after fifteen seconds, my boss clicked something and the video changed. As the rest of the team started chuckling at a cat eating with chopsticks, I stood in silence, wondering whether anyone had clocked me laughing at an advert by Save the Children.

Attachment

I emailed the team asking them to look over a document, but forgot to attach it. I immediately emailed again, joking about how maybe I should try actually attaching it this time (!). I forgot to attach it to that too, so I emailed again, joking about how I had clearly not woken up yet and promising that the document was now attached. Instead of the document, I accidentally attached a short story I was working on about a man who hates his job and colleagues. I emailed again, finally attaching the correct document and apologising for my obvious attachment issues.

A Short Play about Marital Tension

HUSBAND: Do you fancy driving tonight?

WIFE: No.

HUSBAND: I suppose it's my turn, is it?

WIFE: Was that sarcastic?

HUSBAND: Yes. I always drive.

WIFE: There's no need for that.

HUSBAND: But you're *driving* me mad.

WIFE: Ha ha.

[As the curtain falls, they embrace to the tune of 'It's Not Unusual' by Tom Jones]

Reception

I have a recurring dream in which I attend my own post-funeral drinks reception. All of my Facebook friends are there (I must have made an event). There is a table of sandwiches and soft drinks. There is no atmosphere. People have naturally split into groups; school friends, university friends, colleagues. I encourage them to mingle but they ignore me. Even my mother and my brother look bored, perhaps because my father is not there (he is not on Facebook). I spy my girl-friend by the sandwiches, deciding between ham and cheese and egg and cress. I suggest egg and cress but she goes for ham and cheese.

Never Have I Ever

Never have I ever done it up the bum. Never have I ever done it in public. Never have I ever had a threesome.

My turn was approaching fast and inside I was panicking. It was my first night in my university halls and my reputation for the next three years depended on what I was about to say, sitting here in a sixteen-strong circle on the kitchen floor. But what should I say? In the last ten minutes my sex life had begun to look exotically bland. Should I make something up? Never have I ever done it in a tractor? On a horse? Never have I ever done a horse? Desperate for inspiration, I took a swig of my Tesco Bière Spéciale.

You've done it in a coffin, mate?!

What?

I forgot that I wasn't supposed to drink unless I'd done the thing that had just been said.

Oh, I mean yeah, mate. All the time.

Only three turns until me. Only three turns until me and I still didn't know what to say! It had to be sexual, that's the point, isn't it? Never have I ever done a model… a man… a milkman… never have I ever done it in a shop… a shopping trolley… a shopping basket…

Hang on a minute. This wasn't why I came to university. I didn't come here to try and fit in with my sex stories, I was studying English Literature for God's sake! I came here to sip whisky and talk about Camus with my new friends, listen to Leonard Cohen late into the night, pass a guitar round, maybe pop outside for a social smoke or two in my new duffel coat. I'd been watching YouTube tutorials on how to roll! Why should I make up sex stories to try and fit in? I didn't come here to fit in! I came here to be different!

The group cheered again, I didn't catch the last one. Then Martin piped up to my left. He was drunk.

Never have I ever been caught wanking by my Mum.

Everybody laughed. A few people took sheepish sips. Then the laugher began to subside. I was next. I was next and I still didn't know what I was going to say! I needed to show them that I was the thinker of the group, the writer. I had to say something witty, show them that I was above such games, in a different league intellectually but also good fun to have around. But I couldn't think! I'd had too much to drink! I needed time! I needed more time!

What did your Mum catch you wanking over, Martin?

Yes! Time! I had mere seconds to think of what to say while Martin slurred something about YouPorn. Then it was my turn, the circle fell silent and all ears were on me. It was my turn to show them what I'd got.

Never have I ever thought this game was very clever.

I took a triumphant swig of my Bière Spéciale. The mood never quite recovered.

Podcast

I accidentally bought a pair of industrial ear defenders, thinking that they were wireless headphones. I knew that they would be useless for listening to podcasts but I tried them on anyway and discovered that while all external noise was silenced, my own voice was brilliantly clear. I now present and listen to my own podcast by going for long walks and talking to myself while wearing them. It is quite intellectual but also very funny.

Discussed

I discovered that no email can be questioned that starts with the phrase *as discussed*. I used my new power responsibly at first – claiming a refund here, wrangling an extra gigabyte of data there. But before long, I was demanding free holidays, VIP concert passes and even a prototype Ferrari which I'm about to drive to Justin Bieber's house. We're going to make a roast, play N64 and then get drunk and slag off One Direction. Tina Turner will be joining us for the last part, as discussed.

Inflight Fight

Do you need a wee before we land?

No.

I know what you're like.

I don't need a wee.

Well, it doesn't matter now. The seatbelt lights are on.

You what?

Put your seatbelt on, we're landing.

Oh, right. I think I need a wee.

Well, you can't now.

Do you think there'll be a toilet when we land?

I don't know, Jim, I didn't design the airport.

Name

Keen to be treated with more respect, I applied to add a blue tick to my name via deed poll. I was informed over the phone that icons were not permitted so I changed my surname to Blue-Tick instead. After finding myself constantly correcting those who misheard my name as Blu Tack or Blue Tit, I telephoned again, changing my surname to Verified. I took great pride in introducing myself to people, but soon realised that many were now mishearing my name as Terrified. When the paperwork arrived, I discovered that the operator had also misheard me, and that only two name changes are allowed in any ten-year period.

The Scoff Gang

Extract from 'Daniel Piper is in Four Gangs' (2016)

I joined my first gang when I was five years old. It was called the Scoff Gang.

The Scoff Gang was me and my brother (he was eight). My job was to sneak downstairs in the middle of the night and steal Munch Bunch yoghurts from the fridge and bring them up to him. His job was to eat them. And, he said, deal with the admin.

It was very much a two-man operation: me downstairs in the field, stealing the yoghurts, and my brother James (or Sergeant Scoff) in his bedroom (or office [or scoffice]), making sure everything was running smoothly.

We were good. For two years it was successful mission after successful mission. And you know what? The adrenaline never went away. The adrenaline, and the fear. The fear of being caught. By Mum. I was good, alright. I was the best. But I wasn't quite good enough.

I'll never forget my last mission. It began like any other. I waited until I could hear Mum snoring, then crept across the landing to the scoffice for the briefing.

'You're late.' He didn't even lift his head from his *Beano*.

'Apologies, Sergeant Scoff. She took a while to begin snoring tonight.'

'Sit down.'

I sat myself down on his inflatable chair.

'I'll get straight to business,' he said. 'Are you familiar with Sally Strawberry?'

Sally was a yoghurt. He'd never asked for her before (usually it was

Andy Apricot). I had heard that Sally was the tastiest of all the Munch Bunch. I kept my cool.

'I've heard of her,' I said. 'But we haven't met personally.'

'Well, it's time for that to change. I want you to bring her to me. There's just one small complication. Are you familiar with Mike Piper?' (Mike Piper is our Dad.)

'I've heard of him,' I said. 'Mum's husband. Dangerous, but not bright.'

'Correct. I believe he is still in the living room, watching a repeat of *Ballykissangel*. You will have to be careful.'

And with that, I was back on the landing. I skilfully timed the creaky floorboard with the rhythm of Mum's snoring then crept down the stairs, skilfully stepping only on the edges to minimise noise. At the bottom, I looked from right to left (skilfully). To my left was the living room – Dad. The door was slightly ajar. He was making some sort of sound. Laughing? Crying? He was... he was snoring! This was going to be easier than I thought!

I opened the kitchen door and closed it behind me (skilfully), then crept over to the fridge, skilfully opening the door. And there they all were. Third shelf. Andy Apricot. Barney Banana. Bertie Blackcurrant. Ollie Orange. Rozzy Raspberry. Sally Strawberry. The Munch Bunch. I reached in and skilfully detached Sally from Barney.

Sally Strawberry. The tastiest of all the Munch Bunch. As I held her, I was momentarily entranced by her. The round redness of her face, sprinkled with teasing flecks of seed. Those plump, juicy, ever-so-slightly pouting lips. The green leaf above her head tied into a playful bow. Those soft, delicate eyelashes fluttering over those eyes... those come-to-fridge eyes.

My fingers crept almost involuntarily towards her lid. Just one spoonful. Sergeant Scoff need never know. To hell with Sergeant Scoff! Why should he have her? I should have her! Right here, right now! On the kitchen table! Or here, standing against the fridge!

Get a hold of yourself, Agent Scoff! I slapped myself awake. *Never let the girl come before the mission!*

I pulled her from the fridge and ran upstairs. I was halfway up when

I realised... the spoon! I'd forgotten the spoon! I ran back without even checking the living room. I opened the drawer, I took the spoon, I closed the drawer, I turned around and...

'Well, well, well...' It was Dad! He was standing in the doorway of the kitchen! I ran at him and attempted to dive through his legs but he was too quick – he caught me and lifted me into the air. I threw a sharp left hook at his face which he parried, but my second punch landed squarely on his jaw. He dropped me to the floor and I skilfully jack-knifed to my feet. He lunged towards me again but I dodged the attack with a skilful forward roll, sending him careering into the glass table, which smashed into hundreds of tiny pieces. He pulled a bloodied shard from his leg and glared angrily at the wound. I picked up my own piece of glass and for a few seconds we sparred with the pieces of glass, then he grabbed my arm and twisted it behind my back. I dropped my shard but then skilfully elbowed him in the chest. Seconds later, I was crashing into the fridge door. He threw a punch, but I skilfully ducked, leaving a huge dent in the door.

It was then that I realised that Sally was no longer in my hand. She was on the floor! I reached for her but Dad lifted me into the air by my neck. He opened his mouth and (I forgot to mention, he has metal teeth) brought his teeth towards my neck. I threw a punch. No effect! The teeth were getting closer! I reached around for a weapon. Nothing! Closer! I threw another punch! No effect! I hooked my foot underneath Sally Strawberry and kicked her into the air. I caught her and squeezed her, ejecting her content into Dad's eyes.

'Aargh!!'

He was blinded! And almost knocked out. I kicked him. He was knocked out. I looked down at him and simply said, 'Yoghurt to be better than that.'

Another successful mission. But wait... Sally. I uncurled my fingers. My love. Crushed. Empty. Dead. Then I heard a sound from upstairs. Mum. I had woken her up. I had failed.

In that moment, I vowed never to join another gang. But gangs just seem to follow me around. Like a bad smell (of gangs).

i did a wee in a hot tub
i thought the others wouldn't notice
but i'd had a berocca that morning
so they did

Muted

I visited Facebook on my girlfriend's phone to check how my new photo looked on her smaller screen. I couldn't find it, so she admitted that she had muted me. You're pretty dull on there and you post too much, she said. You're much more interesting in real life. Unsure whether to feel offended or flattered, I posted a Twitter poll which received two votes (one for flattered and one for offended).

Whodunnit

In the small town of Ilkeston, Derbyshire, a young boy called George was murdered. Although the police quickly worked out who did it, they refused to reveal the killer's identity for a month.

It's a murder mystery! They announced on the Derbyshire Constabulary Facebook page. *Simply like and share this post, and comment below saying who you think did it. We'll announce a winner on 22 March.*

Throughout the month, the police scheduled some *Possible Suspect* animated GIFs on their Facebook page. These included Martin Candle (the school chef), Barry Sidwell (a local priest) and even George's own mother, Denise. A picture of each suspect was accompanied by a list of potential motives (all made up by the police).

On 22 March, a huge crowd gathered outside the town hall to watch the chief constable announce the killer's identity.

And the killer is...

The crowd fell silent. One man shouted *Find out after the break*, which got a big laugh. The chief constable finally revealed that the killer was Declan Scrivins and the winner of the Facebook competition was Martin Candle. Denise was allowed to place the handcuffs on Declan's wrists.

I honestly thought it would be Barry Sidwell! she exclaimed as she turned the key.

That month, the Derbyshire Constabulary Facebook page saw a 9% increase in engagement, with an organic reach of over 4,000. The page received 42 new likes.

your love
was as true
as an email
which says

sorry for the delayed response, it's been a really busy few weeks

Wars

I wrote to George Lucas, complaining that the *Star Wars* films were scientifically inaccurate, because there is no sound in space. He thanked me for my letter and told me to watch this space – the originals were due another remaster. A few months later, a new *Ultimate Final Director's Cut* of the original trilogy was released. I was intrigued to see whether Lucas had heeded my advice and removed the sound from the space battles. It turned out that he had in fact entirely removed any reference to space from the films. No space battles, no dialogue about space, even the word *Star* had been removed from the title. The films no longer made any sense. I felt kind of bad.

Poem for My Hairdresser

you brought me
a drink

but there was no
appropriate moment
to take
a sip

An Exchange

WOMAN: There was a mouse in the house yesterday. I tried to catch it but it disappeared.

MAN: Oh, my! Did you find it?

WOMAN: Yes, I eventually found it dead inside my printer.

MAN: Ha ha! Did the box for the printer say 'also doubles as a mouse-trap?'

WOMAN: No.

[Curtain]

Extraordinary

I visited a clothing store and took the escalator to the first floor. After a few minutes, I discovered that there was no escalator back down, only stairs. It was almost as though the store cared less about departing customers than arriving ones. I approached a sales assistant and demanded to be carried down the stairs. When they refused, I decided to take drastic action and descend the upwards escalator. As I exhaustedly exited the store forty minutes later, I wondered whether any customers had filmed this extraordinary act of defiance.

Economics

After years of hearing my favourite artists attribute their genius to the London School of Economics, I signed up for a four-year degree in Business Management and Accounting. On the eve of our graduation, my coursemates and I had drinks in the City. When the conversation turned to why we each wanted to become an accountant, I explained that I was hoping it would inspire me to create great art. The group were hysterical and told me that Huxley, The Beatles et al. were referring to LSD, not LSE. I asked if anyone had any LSD but nobody did (although Jeremy had some coke).

Lottery

I'd like to put five pounds on my Oyster Card please.

Will you be paying by card?

Yes.

Then there will be a 50p charge.

I see. Should I add more, or is there always a 50p charge regardless of the top-up amount?

Yes. You could top up with a million pounds and there would still be a 50p charge.

A million pounds! Ha! I wish!

Maybe if you win the lottery, eh?

Ha! Yes! Maybe!

Although if you did, you probably wouldn't want to put it all on your Oyster card.

Ha! No! Probably not!

Do one thing every day that scares you.

[Within reason. Keep it safe and sensible – I'm not saying you should put your hand in the toaster just because it scares you. Also, don't feel the need to think big. I'm not expecting you to go skydiving or kayaking every day; that would be a huge drain on your time and money. Think small and achievable. For example, I've had an irrational fear of Postman Pat since childhood, so I'm currently trying to watch an episode a day.]

Booking

I had been feeling stressed so I took a week off work to enjoy a relaxing mini-break. After a quick browse on booking.com I found a lovely and secluded spa retreat and decided to book straight away. I was immediately inundated with several flashing messages telling me that this was the very last room available, somebody else had booked a room three nanoseconds ago and there were currently seven billion people looking at the same room as me. I spent my week off in hospital, recovering from the eight panic attacks (and hernia) I suffered during the booking process.

A Short Play about Cooking

[Ten COOKS are stirring a broth]

COOK 8 [to COOK 3]: You're spoiling it.

[Curtain]

TV

People are always asking if I watch this or that TV show, but I'm intimidated by the idea of starting something from the beginning when there are often tens, sometimes even hundreds, of hours of screen time ahead. That said, I've just finished episode four of *Coronation Street* and am already beginning to see what all the fuss is about.

Movie

After reading that sales of the *Oxford English Dictionary* were falling, I decided that the time was right to approach them with my proposed screenplay for a movie adaptation of the book. It featured a large ensemble cast each playing a different word and was pitched as *Noam Chomsky meets The Emoji Movie*. They didn't respond so I contacted them again, this time attaching my proposed poster and movie tie-in book cover (featuring me in the lead role). They still didn't respond so I gave up. A few months later, I was shocked and appalled to discover a poster for *Dictionary*, starring Matt Damon as The.

Sales Meeting

We are all sitting around the Big Table, looking at the Big Spreadsheet. Some items are green because they are making more money than last week. Some items are red because they are making less money than last week. Some items are orange because they are making the same amount of money as last week. The Big Spreadsheet has many more meanings, deeper meanings. But I do not understand these meanings because I am new and this is my first sales meeting.

To my left, Richard is sweating. He is trying to explain to the rest of the team why his item is red. The team are shaking their heads and tutting professionally. I feel sorry for Richard. Apart from me, he is the newest and youngest addition to the Big Table and is eager to impress. But Richard speaks too quickly. His brain cannot keep up with his mouth so he fills the gaps with phrases like with regards to, as opposed to and on the basis that.

To my right, flatulent manager Harriet raises both eyebrows.

Tell us, Richard. Why are you red this week?

Well, with regards to... as opposed to... on the basis that...

We ought to call you *Red Richard.*

The group chuckle professionally.

Red Richard: Sales Dimwit.

Richard is almost in tears. Harriet reaches across and points at the red item. It is in the bottom right corner of the Big Spreadsheet, right under my nose.

We can't have this, Red Richard. We simply can't have this.

I gather up a large mouthful of saliva and open my mouth, letting it fall slowly onto Harriet's hand. Everyone falls silent and watches the saliva slide down her hand and onto the table. Harriet, unable to comprehend what has just happened, simply stares in disbelief at the soiled spreadsheet.

T-Shirt

I was inspired to go into T-shirt design after seeing a man who was wearing one with *FBI: Female Body Inspector* printed on the front. I launched my first two designs last month and am already concerned that I may have misjudged the tone. Sales of *CIA: Creepy, Insecure And [Disrespectful]* are poor, and *LAPD: Look, A Penis! Did [You Not Want To See It? Oh Well, Too Late Now]* is doing even worse.

A Short Play about Two Dinosaurs

DINOSAUR 1: Rargh!

DINOSAUR 2: Rargh!

[Curtain]

Translation:

DINOSAUR 1: Last night's party was a roaring success!

DINOSAUR 2: Ha! Roaring! That's good. I like that.

Some Notes from My Writing Notebook Which No Longer Mean Anything to Me

- daniel radcliffe speech impediment
- condom changing room (ASK FOR SMALLER SIZE)
- 'Shit happens. Shappens.'
- old woman completely OBSESSED with mahjong
- doctor and husband and curtain and wife
- Twisted Butter Licker
- prince harry married meghan markle by accident (meant to marry angela merkel)
- hash moustache
- simon cowell insecurities
- drinking mulled wine on lunch break (+ getting TIPSY)
- getting star struck by strangers
- superpower: getting up early
- reading poem out loud + farting on every full stop
- murderous lollipop lady (deliberately walks children in front of cars lol)
- finding rustling paper erotic
- making a joke so funny it brings the plane down (ie. brings the house down, but on a plane – LOL.)

Ten

Theresa May warned her husband not to use the bathroom for at least ten minutes. Number Two? he asked. You could call this one a Number Ten! she shouted back. As she sprayed some Febreze, Theresa chuckled to herself and wondered whether any other Prime Ministers had ever made the same quip while living at this address.

Doctor

I had been feeling paranoid lately so I visited the doctor. After I sat down, he asked what seemed to be the problem. I couldn't believe it. I had half a mind to tell him that what *seemed* to be the problem was the fact that Doctor Robertson over here *seemed* to think that he was somehow better than me, that whatever I thought the problem was actually only *seemed* to be the problem and that he was somehow qualified to tell me what the real problem was. I decided not to rise to it. I simply stood up, announced that I seemed to have chosen the wrong doctor, and left.

Wild

My girlfriend said that I was too uptight and repressed, that she was looking for someone more adventurous. Desperate to show her my wild side, I took my phone from my pocket and removed the case. That's not what I mean, she said. I want somebody passionate, somebody who isn't afraid to, you know, go all the way. I knew what she meant. I took a deep breath and removed the screen protector. I immediately regretted it. As she gathered her things around me, I reapplied the protector and began furiously smoothing out the bubbles.

i was laughed at
at big school
for calling breaktime
playtime

perhaps i wasn't ready
to stop playing
and start needing a break.

Kindle

In an attempt to read more, I bought a Kindle. I couldn't work out how to use it, though, so I bought a copy of *Kindle for Dummies*. It was only available for Kindle, so I bought a copy of *Kindle for Dummies for Dummies*, which was also only available for Kindle. Eventually I found a paper copy of *Kindle for Dummies for Dummies for Dummies for Dummies for Dummies*. I've just got to the end of *Kindle for Dummies for Dummies for Dummies* and am hoping to eventually read a novel next year.

Game

One of my childhood computer games featured a voice which, if I spent too long selecting a vehicle, yelled at me to hurry up. Of the voice's many admonishments, my favourite was, What are you waiting for? Christmas?! On 24 December 1998, I did something that I had been plotting for months. I loaded up the vehicle selection screen at 11.58pm, waited for that particular complaint, shouted, Actually, yes!! then started the game a moment later at midnight. It remains the greatest thing I have ever done.

Jesus's Jokes

Jesus was many things. Carpenter. Miracle worker. Son. But not a lot of people know that as well as these things, he was also a bit of a comedian.

He liked to make little quips every now and again. For example, after he'd turned the water into wine and was handing it out to partygoers, one man asked if there was definitely enough for everyone. Quick as a flash, Jesus turned to him and said, Stop wining!

It was jokes like this that made him so popular. They always hit the spot. The only jokes that didn't work so well were the ones set in the future (as Jesus could see into the future but his disciples couldn't). But the rest worked every time.

After feeding the five thousand, Jesus asked Peter whether everyone had eaten.

I think so, said Peter.

Phew! said Jesus. That's a loaf off my mind.

Even when faced with his imminent death, Jesus was still cracking zingers. As a crowd of spectators gathered under his outstretched body, he looked down and simply said, I'll have you all know, I'm feeling very cross about all this!

But the laughs didn't stop there. When Mary Magdalene caught sight of the recently resurrected Jesus, she cried, I thought you were dead!

Oh, no, Jesus quipped, I was just having a rest. I was dead tired.

Mary burst out laughing, and Jesus patted her on the back.

Don't worry, Mary, he said, I've got your back.

Mary snorted. You're full of them today, Jesus! she said, slapping him on the bum.

Ooh! said Jesus. I quite enjoyed that. Shall I turn the other cheek?

Mary doubled over.

Come on, said Jesus, let's go and surprise the disciples.

They couldn't believe their eyes. We thought you were dead! they cried.

Oh, no, Jesus quipped, I was just having a rest. I was dead tired.

The disciples immediately fell about laughing, as did Mary.

And she's heard it before! said Jesus.

As the laughter died down, Jesus thought of another joke. It was set in the future. Jesus knew he would need to give it some context first so he spent the next half an hour explaining the concept of the mobile phone to the disciples.

When he was confident that the joke was definitely going to work, he said, if you still don't believe I'm real, you can take a photo of me. You could even set it as your screensaver. Or should I say, screen saviour.

The disciples did laugh, but it was a polite, slightly confused laugh and Jesus would be lying if he said he wasn't a bit disappointed. He wasn't too hard on himself, though. He'd had an extremely stressful few days and the fact that he was making jokes at all was quite impressive.

Halloween

Having recently embraced travelling alone, dining alone and even going to the cinema alone, I decided to try trick-or-treating alone. The first five people who opened the door refused to give me any sweets so I turned around, disappointed. I went back home, took off my pumpkin costume and decided to try again in a few months when it was Halloween.

you can enter
any door
if you are carrying
a chair

(Honestly, try it. They'll let you in.)

TV

I went to the supermarket during Black Friday, picked up a sixty-inch TV and waited for another shopper to attack. Nobody took any notice, so I carried it around the store for a while, murmuring things like 'stay back' and 'it's mine'. I then took it to the checkout in the hope that it would spur somebody into assaulting me and taking it but they didn't, even as I theatrically misremembered my PIN. Panicking that I might actually have to buy the TV, I punched myself in the face, blamed the old lady queueing behind me and left the store, complaining loudly about capitalism today.

A Short Play about Decisions

[JUDY and JEFF are in a sex shop, looking at costumes]

JUDY: Dominatrix or nurse?

JEFF: Decisions, decisions…

JUDY: Jeff!

JEFF: What?

JUDY: Don't you read the news? The government have replaced the phrase 'decisions, decisions' with something more efficient.

JEFF: Oh. What should I say, then?

JUDY: Like before, but eight times. 'Decisions, decisions, decisions, decisions, decisions, decisions, decisions, decisions.'

JEFF: Oh.

JUDY: So, dominatrix or nurse?

JEFF: Erm, decisions, decisions, decisions, decisions, decisions, decisions, decisions.

[JUDY glares at JEFF]

JEFF: …decisions.

JUDY: Ha, I know what you mean!

[Curtain]

we all fear the day
that there are no jobs left
because the robots have taken them all

only the comedians will survive
the robots may drive cars
write books and even sing

but they will never master
the noble art
of laugher

[I am now laughing at the image of a robot doing stand-up so maybe I'm wrong actually]

Cold

In the past, whenever anybody coughed or sneezed in my vicinity, I became immediately anxious about catching their illness. Public transport was a particular ordeal and I spent many a journey mentally cancelling weeks' worth of plans due to a nearby nose-blower. Then, one day, I realised that the real problem was my own. It was I who needed to change. These days, if anybody coughs or sneezes in my vicinity, I always rush towards them and passionately kiss them. In the last two years I haven't once worried about catching a cold (because I have always had one).

Phone

I took my phone out of my pocket on the bus and a group of children laughed at me. He's only got an iPhone 4! they jeered. Horrified, I rushed to the shop and bought a new one. The same children were on the bus home, so I proudly flashed my new purchase. Oh God, we didn't mean for you to buy the latest model, one of them said. It's ludicrously expensive. We thought you might get something sensible and mid-range like the 6S. They seemed genuinely concerned.

Famous

In an attempt to become famous, I leaked a nude photograph of myself to a national newspaper. They emailed back within a few minutes, asking if I was famous. I responded cryptically, urging them to publish the image and find out for themselves. They didn't email back. I'm assuming no news is good news and have warned my parents not to buy tomorrow's paper.

Some Eamonn Holmes Ideas

- A story about Eamonn Holmes being cloned (title: *Eamonn Clones*).
- A detective story in which Eamonn Holmes says, *Who needs Sherlock Holmes when you've got Eamonn Holmes?*
- A short story in which all directional signs are removed from an international airport for 24 hours causing complete pandemonium and resulting in many people flying to the wrong destination (including Eamonn Holmes).
- A short story in which Eamonn Holmes makes an impassioned speech to a large crowd and is met with chants of *Amen Holmes!*
- A TV show in which Eamonn Holmes is trapped underneath a giant hammer which could fall at any moment (title: *Holmes Under the Hammer*).

Opinion

My girlfriend said I talk too much. This came as a shock; I *do* have a lot of opinions, but I thought she enjoyed hearing them (because they are always right). That night, while watching Netflix, we came up with a solution. My opinions are now presented in an auto-play format: whenever I have finished sharing one, I will announce, *Next opinion starting in ten... nine... eight...* etc., during which she can say *Stop* at any time. She nearly always does, but it's a fair and democratic system. And that's what matters, in my opinion.

A Short Play about Heaven

[DEREK is sitting in front of a RECEPTIONIST]

RECEPTIONIST: Hello, Derek. Welcome to heaven.

DEREK: Oh, am I dead?

RECEPTIONIST: Yes, you died two minutes ago.

DEREK: Oh. Is Mary ok?

RECEPTIONIST: Let's have a look, shall we?

[The RECEPTIONIST clicks the mouse]

—Ah, yes, there she is. She's at your bedside. The doctors are leading her away. She's going for it with those tears, bless her!

DEREK: Oh dear.

RECEPTIONIST: Right, then. Before you can enter heaven, we need to select your look.

DEREK: Pardon?

RECEPTIONIST: Well, heaven's supposed to be nice isn't it? We can't have you looking like a teabag. If everybody looked like they did at the moment of death, then heaven would be full of old, ill and injured people! We need to select your look before you can enter.

DEREK: How?

RECEPTIONIST: We'll just need to log in to your Facebook account.

DEREK: I don't have Facebook.

RECEPTIONIST: Surely your daughter made you an account?

DEREK: She did, but I never used it.

RECEPTIONIST: Can you remember the login details?

DEREK: No. I don't understand; why do we need them?

RECEPTIONIST: We need to go through your Facebook photos to select your look. Without the login details we can't select your look and without a look you can't enter heaven.

DEREK: Even if I could remember the details, I doubt there are any photos on there.

RECEPTIONIST: What is this, the Stone Age? You don't have any photos on Facebook? What is this, the Bronze Age?

DEREK: I do have a box of old photographs in the attic.

RECEPTIONIST: Ah, perfect!

DEREK: Really?

RECEPTIONIST: Let's just log in to your attic, shall we?

DEREK: Sorry?

RECEPTIONIST: Of course that's no use! What are you going to do, go home and grab them? You're dead, you fool!

DEREK: Well there's no need for—

RECEPTIONIST: I haven't got time for this. I'm fed up with people like you. This is supposed to be a five-minute procedure: *Ok, let's look at your Facebook photos. Here, you looked nice at Sarah's 21st birthday bash, shall we go for that? Ok, off you go!* But no, I still get people like you with your *Ooh, sorry, I don't use Facebook*, wasting my time. Go on, go.

DEREK: What?

RECEPTIONIST: You see that door? The one with the big sign that says *Hell*? That's your door. Hurry up. And here, take this.

[The RECEPTIONIST throws a bottle of sun lotion to DEREK]

DEREK: What's this for?

RECEPTIONIST: Let's just say it might get hot in there.

[Curtain]

Prompt

I was feeling down and uninspired so I bought a book of writing prompts which contained over two hundred opening sentence suggestions. I closed my eyes, opened a page at random and pointed at a sentence. It read, *I was feeling down and uninspired so I bought a book of writing prompts which contained over two hundred opening sentence suggestions.* I chose a different sentence instead and ended up writing a brilliant story about a penguin who learns to code.

Bohemian

I was invited to attend a prestigious literary event (as a plus-one). Anxious to make an impression, I decided to dress in a dandyish and bohemian fashion. As most of my clothes are either brown or black, I opted for odd socks. During the event, nobody seemed to notice – everyone was more interested in Ian McEwan's beret. In an attempt to highlight my socks, I went to the toilet and removed my trousers. It worked; I received several glances on my return. The next morning, I sent my manuscript to every publisher who had been present, cryptically signed: *The author with one brown and one black sock ;)*

i feel like gatsby
standing at the top of this hill
in the dead of night
staring at a small green light
on the city horizon

but this is not america
it's leamington spa
and i'm not gatsby (i'm just me)
and the small green light is not a symbol
of my passionate unrequited love
it's asda

Power

After reading several stories of famous people (Rihanna, a Kardashian) wiping billions from companies' stock value with a single negative tweet, I decided to give it a go myself. I chose a large, morally dubious corporation and wrote a scathing tweet about it to my two hundred followers. That evening, at the supermarket, I noticed that large bottles of Coca-Cola were half price. At first I was taken aback by my own power, but this was quickly replaced by an overwhelming sense of responsibility. I rushed home and immediately began plotting who to bring down next.

Apps

I downloaded an app which measured the time I spent looking at my phone per day. It was far too easy. I managed to complete it on the third day with the maximum possible score (twenty-four hours). I then moved on to a sleep tracking app. This was a little more difficult but I eventually achieved the same score after a few weeks of sleep deprivation (and with the help of some pills). Right now I'm playing one which counts my daily calories. It's definitely the hardest of the three. Yesterday I ate forty French Fancies with no sign of the game ending. Today I try fifty.

A Short Play about a Test

[MARTIN is sitting at the kitchen table. JOHN bursts through the door]

MARTIN: Oh, hi, John.

JOHN: It's a test.

MARTIN: What?

JOHN: It's a test.

MARTIN: What is?

JOHN: It's a test.

[As the curtain falls, ushers hand each audience member a mental arithmetic test which they must complete in silence. Anybody who scores less than 90% receives the cane as they exit the theatre]

Tattoo

In an attempt to become more attractive, I visited my local tattoo parlour. The tattooist asked what I wanted and I told her I didn't know, I thought it was random. She suggested I go home, write down some phrases or lyrics I liked and come back tomorrow. I couldn't think of anything so I clicked Random Article on Wikipedia twenty times and wrote the titles down. We ran through the list together and narrowed it down to two. I couldn't choose between them so I went for both: *List of inventors killed by their own inventions* on my left shoulder and *Mysterious Girl (Peter Andre song)* down my right leg.

Millennial

Tired of being told to choose between eating avocado and owning a house, I decided to build a house made entirely out of avocado. It had avocado walls, avocado furniture, an avocado record player and even avocado plates to hold my morning avocado toast (which was a toast-shaped piece of avocado topped with avocado). My father came to visit and seemed impressed by my new set-up, but then had to go and ruin it by asking if I had a car, though. He tried acting like it was some clever play on the word avocado, but I told him that whatever my generation does, it will never be enough, will it.

we all
have one memory
too painful
to forget

(mine is when the dj at my james bond-themed birthday party opened
with the mission impossible theme tune)

Model

After hearing that many rich and famous models are first spotted on the street by talent scouts, I caught the train to London and walked around Soho for several hours. It grew dark and I was close to giving up when a police officer approached, demanding to know why I was hanging around street corners at night. I explained that I was merely offering my services, so he arrested me. At first I was mortified, but my horror turned to joy when he took my photograph at the station. He was simply trying to help. At that moment, I realised that life's most meaningful pursuit is not money or fame. It's kindness.

Vegetable Rap

This piece is dedicated to Rhymes With Orange, the brilliant poetry collective and performance night in London that I am very lucky to be part of. The poem was written during one of our annual writing retreats in the middle of bloody nowhere, specifically the one where I forgot to respond to the 'dietary requirements' text with news of my recent switch to vegetarianism and found myself rationing a cold frittata for four difficult days.

***

I'm vegetarian now
I don't eat meat no more
I don't need meat no more
Give me a piece of meat
and I'll just throw it on the floor

I'm vegetarian
I ain't going *there* again (*there* is KFC)
'cause when it comes to meat-eating
I'm disestablishmentarian

Where once I ate chicken
I now eat chickpeas
and when I see someone eating chicken
I feel compelled to flick Vs

I've got beef
with beef
and when I see it I go mental
The only thing that'll calm me down
is a bowl of bloody lentils

So make no mistake
I don't want no mincemeat
'cause I don't miss steak
and I don't miss meat

He doesn't eat meat
'cause he's a flippin' ledge
he goes by the name
DJ Veg

I find pheasant unpleasant
I think lamb is a sham
I don't want chicken for no lickin'
fuck parma ham

I'm not a glutton for mutton
meat doesn't give me the horn
I don't want partridge in my arteries
my porn is Quorn

He doesn't eat meat
'cause he's a flippin' ledge
he goes by the name
DJ Veg

I have frittata for starter
I have frittata for main
I have frittata for dessert
and then frittata again

People say
DJ Veg, does it all taste the same?

Of course it bloody does!
it's driving me insane!

He doesn't eat meat
'cause he's a flippin' ledge
he goes by the name
DJ Veg

I find pheasant pleasant
I don't think lamb is a sham
I want some chicken for some lickin'
I want to fuck parma ham

I'm a glutton for mutton
meat really gives me the horn
I want some partridge in my arteries
My porn is NOT Quorn.
What even is Quorn? It's like eating cardboard. It's like smoking a
cigarette that isn't lit. It's like drinking a non-alcoholic beer.

I've made a mistake
I've made a mistake
I've made a mistake
I really miss steak

Pleasant

As she returned my hand luggage, the security officer wished me a pleasant night. You too, I replied. She rolled her eyes and walked away. Heading towards the departure gate, I realised that she had wished me a pleasant flight, not night. How could I have been so stupid? She wasn't flying anywhere. She was a security officer. In the end, the flight wasn't pleasant at all. We encountered very heavy turbulence and were forced to perform an emergency landing. The lady next to me helped me to inflate my life jacket, and instead of saying *thanks a lot*, I accidentally said *thank you a lot*.

Concerto

I attended a live piano concerto and was enjoying it until I noticed that the pianist was reading from an iPad. It was not connected to a power supply and I became instantly anxious that he may have forgotten to charge it sufficiently for the ninety-minute performance. I crept silently onto the stage and, without him noticing, connected my external power bank to the device. The pianist then dramatically tapped the screen (which I later discovered turns the page). I was concerned that I might have crashed his iPad, so I leapt up and performed a hard reset.

Wednesday Weekend

I've just got a new job. It's great. The only problem is that I only get one day off a week. But that's okay, it just means that Wednesday is my weekend.

***

Every Wednesday, I wake up at 10.15am. At 10.25, I have a shower. At 10.40am, I go downstairs and make breakfast. Then, at 11am, I start pre-drinking. Four cans of Red Stripe in the kitchen. I then make my way into the living room to play Ring of Fire (the drinking game [not the song]) in front of *Loose Women*. Depending on the cards, I'm usually tipsy by 12.15, so I go for a wee then leave the house.

There are no clubs open on a Wednesday lunchtime so I go to the cafe down the road. Fortunately, it's one of those trendy new cafes that serve alcohol. I order four double vodka and Red Bulls and drink them in the corner while listening to trance music on my headphones.

By 2pm, I'm usually battered. Sometimes I'll be up on my feet having a little dance in the corner, or sometimes I just sit there. It all depends on what kind of drunk I am. If it's the latter kind, I'll often call my ex-girlfriend on the way home. If she's on her lunch break, she sometimes answers and says things like, What the hell is happening to you, it's 2pm on a Wednesday lunchtime and you're drunk. And I'll say something funny like, It's the freakin' weekend baby, I'm having me some fun.

At 3pm, fully clothed, I collapse onto my bed.

At 6pm, I wake with a hangover. At 6.15pm I drag myself downstairs and prepare a Sunday roast. I pop it in the oven, set the timer for two hours and then head to church. It's always quite empty, which I find disappointing. I keep asking Father Brennan to establish a second Sunday service for those of us with Wednesday weekends but he says there is not enough demand, which I find hard to believe.

I return home at 7.30pm, just in time for my Sunday roast, which I eat at the kitchen table with a copy of last weekend's *Sunday Times*. I then retire to the living room at 8.10 to watch an episode of *Heartbeat* on DVD. I've written to ITV asking them to release *Heartbeat* on Blu-Ray but they say there is not enough demand, which I find hard to believe.

When the episode is over, it's a cup of Horlicks for me and then bed. I set my alarm for 7am and sigh, suddenly full of the Sunday blues.

Fool

After too many years of being made to look like a fool, I made it my new policy not to believe a word anybody said before midday on April 1st. I stormed out of the flat after my girlfriend 'cooked us both breakfast' (two plates for herself was excessive – might I not be hungry too?), then had a fight with Jim at the corner shop over the price of his eggs. Halfway through my own breakfast, a policeman arrived to ask about the fight at the shop. I'm writing this from the station – it is 11.50am. If they are still asking the same questions in ten minutes, I will co-operate. Until then, they are not real police officers and this is not a real station.

Desist

On my last day in the office, during goodbye hugs and well wishes, a few of my colleagues suggested we keep in touch. This was nice of them, I thought, so I made an effort to email every now and again to let them know what I'd been up to, how Auntie Mavis's health was doing and, of course, how I was getting on in my new job. After a few weeks, I received a Cease and Desist notice informing me that *keep in touch* is a formal courtesy, and that my life was no longer the company's concern.

a man was snoring on the train
so i wrote an angry facebook status about him

then i woke him up and read it to him

(we weren't friends, how else was he supposed to see it?)

Facebook

Concerned about privacy, I deleted Facebook. While the absence was refreshing, I soon began compensating for it in my daily life. I would stop strangers and ask to see their holiday photos, show them newspaper headlines (whispering a single word such as *shocking* or *appalling*), and politely suggest that they respond with one of four facial expressions. I knew something was wrong with me after I furiously entered a lingerie shop, insisting that they remove their poorly targeted window display and demanding to know whether I looked like the kind of man who wore women's underwear.

CommanderBond.net

Extract from 'Daniel Piper is in Four Gangs' (2016)

2002. I'm 11 years old and I've been gang free for five years. I'm clean. My life's back on track. I'm a normal guy. I keep my head down. I stay out of trouble.

But that all changed one evening. I was watching *Emmerdale* with my Mum. (I can remember which episode it was: it was the one where Andy Sugden burns down the barn, but he doesn't realise his Mum's still inside and she dies.) During the break, I saw an advert for the James Bond collection on VHS and asked for it for Christmas.

I became obsessed with Bond. I wanted to look like Bond. I wanted to sound like Bond. I began wearing one of my Dad's NatWest work jackets because I thought it looked like a dinner suit. I started gelling my hair into a side parting with his £1 green stuff. I began speaking in a posh Roger Moore accent and trying to learn to raise my eyebrow. I also started to wonder, around this time, whether being fancied by girls might be a good thing.

I obviously didn't know what sex was. I didn't understand any of the sex jokes in the films. For example, in *From Russia with Love*, when Bond says to Russian agent Tatiana Romanova, 'You must be the most beautiful girl I've ever seen.'

And she says, 'I think my mouth is too big.'

And he says, 'No, it's the right size. For me, that is.'

I thought that just meant that he liked big mouths. But I obviously now know that what he really means is: No, it's the right size. Were you to fellate me, there would be no size issues. Perfectly compatible.

Or, in *The Spy Who Loved Me*, when Bond goes to Egypt and is about to sleep with a woman in a pyramid, and she says, 'Are you sure about this, Mr Bond?'

And he says, 'When one is in Egypt, one should delve deeply into its treasures.'

I thought that just meant that when one is in Egypt, one should go to a museum, maybe learn some of the history of the place.

But I obviously now know that what he really means is, when one is in Egypt, one should have sex in a pyramid.

Or in *The World is Not Enough*, at the end of the film, when he's having sex with Dr Christmas Jones and says, 'I thought Christmas only came once a year.'

I thought he was just saying, this is great, this is absolutely brilliant, it's like Christmas!

But I obviously now know that what he really means is, I thought Christmas only... orgasms once... a year. (To be honest, I'm not 100% sure what he really means there.)

Anyway, it was becoming increasingly clear that I could look like Bond and I could sound like Bond, but if I wanted to be like Bond, I needed a girlfriend. The trouble was, none of the girls at Cherry Burton Primary School wanted to talk about Bond. All they wanted to talk about was scented gel pens or The Sims or other things from the 'Who Remembers the Early Noughties?' BuzzFeed list. So I looked elsewhere. I asked Jeeves. And Jeeves told me about the biggest online James Bond fan forum: CommanderBond.net.

I signed up straight away. First, I needed to pick a username. I wanted to show that I knew my Bond but was also a fairly cool guy, so I went for: *i expect u2 die*. My first post was in the 'Introduce yourself' thread:

Hi der Bond fans. My nam is i expect u2 die 11 years old. Wot is ur fav Bond film? Mine is AVTAK[1] but I am exited about DAD[2] coming out next month. I fink i will be brosnans best film because it looks like in the film trailer there is lot of explosions and a hovercraft chase wich der has not been in a Bond film ever. i have never even seen a hovercraft in real life so

1. *A View to a Kill.*
2. *Die Another Day.*

i dnt know if u can drive them in england but if u can i bud like 2 save up 4 one so if anyone knows a website plz let me no. I am also intersted in buying a quad bike.

The first reply came from Blofeld's_Cat:

Greetings, expectant one. Welcome to CommanderBond.net. I do hope your username is not some kind of death threat towards the band U2! (Don't worry, I know it's a quote from Goldfinger.) You are a little young, but everyone is welcome here. I'm afraid I don't know where you could purchase a Hovercraft or indeed a Quad Bike in the UK.

My second post was in 'Vulgar language in the Bond films':

Da swering in da films sends a discomfot thru me, sumtimes in my breath I mutter 'ugh' wen da swering is used in casual sentances. In tomorrw never dies, Eliot Carver telling Stamper to 'Kill those Bast@rds' in tomorrow nevr dies was inappropriate and even immature!!!

I visited CommanderBond.net every evening from then on. We talked about everything to do with Bond – mainly how excited we were for *Die Another Day* to be released next month. But I also some-times used the forum to ask some of life's larger questions. For exam-ple, on 9 February 2002, I asked:

Du u like pineapple on your pizza? I dnt, it iz 2 sweet. It standz out from da rest of da pizza. Also it is 2 slimey.

A few days later, it was Valentine's Day. I was walking to school with my friend Thomas. Thomas was one of those boys who, in retrospect, perhaps did not always tell the truth. He told me that he had received several cards that morning, so many that he was unable to open the front door. He told me that he had received cards from girls in Year Seven, Year Eight, Year Nine, Year Ten, Year Eleven, Year Twelve, Year Thirteen, and a girl at university. He also told me that I had probably not received any (because I was a 'stupid git').

But Thomas was wrong. I had received something. The previous evening, I had posted on CommanderBond.net:

Happy Valentine's Day 4 tomorrow to everyone on CommanderBond.net. I do not like Valentine's Day becos it gets bombarded on u and i hav no girl-frend.

There were three replies. FlemingFan said:

Happy Valentine's Day, Expectant One. At least you have friends here! (Which I'm still annoyed about because I never said I didn't have friends, I said I didn't have a girlfriend.)

There was another reply from Mr Martini:

Not to rub it in too much but last year me and my girlfriend had a lovely weekend at a ski lodge and we recreated the opening scene from The Spy Who Loved Me but without the interruption from M, if you catch my drift. Then after she left, From Russia With Love was on tv so a happy Valentine's Day all round lol. We're not together any more so not sure what I'm doing tomorrow, probably going clubbing.

And Blofeld's_Cat said:

Don't worry, expectant one. You're part of the gang here.

Wait, what? Gang? I didn't sign up for that! That life was behind me! I'd vowed never to join another gang again! I was about to turn the computer off when I noticed a small white star next to the Private

Messages box. I'd never received a private message before! It was from BondBabe2000. The subject line: *Valentine's Day*

Hi Expectant One. I saw ur post and wondered if u wud like 2 b my boyfriend

I kept my cool, and simply replied:

Yes.

I realised I probably should have checked her profile first, so I had a look:

Real Name: BondBabe2000
Gender: Female
Location: Earth
Favourite Bond: Timothy Dalton

That's when I knew she was the one. Timothy Dalton. Timothy Dalton is only your favourite Bond if you're a proper Bond fan. My girlfriend. BondBabe2000. A proper Bond fan.
　　Another message arrived:

gr8. happy valentines day hun.

Hun. I didn't know that word, so I asked Jeeves:

A Hun is a member of the Huns, a confederation of nomadic tribes in Western Asia and Europe in late antiquity.

Me and my girlfriend. Two huns. Two Western Asian nomadic Bond fans in late antiquity. I began my reply:

happy valentines day to u 2 hun lol. Are u excited for Die Another Day on Friday?

No! Too geeky, I needed to say something else, keep it cool, look like I had other things on my mind apart from James Bond. So instead, I said:

Happy Valentine's Day to u 2 hun. do u like pineapple on ur pizza? I dnt.

Five minutes later, she replied:

No hun I dnt, its 2 slimey. BTW Hav u had a girlfriend b4?

I thought of Sally Strawberry.

Yes. but it woz a long time ago.

That morning, at school, Mrs Wigley was waiting at her desk with a small pile of envelopes.

'Settle down, settle down. Thank you to those of you who have submitted anonymous Valentine's Day cards. If I call your name out, please come and collect your anonymous Valentine's Day card or cards. I shall start with the girls. Sarah Adams, you have one. Rebecca Lee, you have one. Kay Shmelka, you have one. Polly Sampson, you have six.' (Of course Polly had six, all the boys fancied her.) 'And now the boys. Adam Cowley, you have four.' (Course he did, he was the best at football.) 'Matthew Beckett, you have three.' (Fastest runner.) And that's it. Oh, hang on. What's this?' She pulled another envelope from under the register. 'It appears that there is one more…'

The whole room gasped. Thomas stood up.

'Ah that'll be for me, miss—'

'—Sit down, Thomas! This card is for… Daniel Piper.'

The whole room gasped (again). Thomas was furious.

'Who gave that stupid git a card?!'

I waited until playtime to open the card. I took it to the cloakroom. It was a Gareth Gates Valentine's Day card. There was a big picture of him smiling on the front. Inside, someone had handwritten the entire lyrics to 'Any One of Us'. Underneath, it said:

Ur cute hun.

Love P.

P? Who was P? It couldn't be… *She* wouldn't want to go out with *me*—

'—Hi Daniel.' It was Rachel Salmon. 'Polly wants me to tell you we're going to Cineworld tomorrow night and you're invited.'

'Cineworld? Tomorrow? Are you going to *Die Another Day*?'

'No, Polly wants to see *Scooby–Doo*.'

'Oh. But, *Die Another Day* comes out tomorrow, I've already got tickets with my Dad for—'

'—Polly says that if you come to *Scooby–Doo* you can sit next to her and you might be able to put your arm round her.'

'Tell Polly I'll be there.'

For the rest of the day I was high as a kite. How had this happened? Yesterday I thought I'd never have a girlfriend, and now Polly wanted to sit next to *me* at the cinema and maybe let me put my arm around her! I felt amazing. I felt like… Bond.

There was just one problem. One thing I needed to get off my chest. That evening, I logged on to CommanderBond.net and posted:

hi guyz. i dnt think i am gna be able 2 see DAD on friday cos im going to scooby doo. its ok tho bcus i am gna go on saturday. just letin u no in case u r wonderin y i am not discussing the film wiv u on friday.

Surely they'd understand. It was just one day later. FlemingFan replied a few minutes later:

This is gravely disappointing news, expectant one. As a member of the largest online James Bond fan forum, we expect a certain level of dedication to the canon. While you may believe it is 'ok' to see the film on Saturday, I'm not sure quite how you intend to join a conversation with members whose opinions have had a day to mature, or who have indeed already seen the film a second time. I urge you to reconsider.

Then Blofeld's_Cat:

I'm afraid I agree with FlemingFan. If you wish to be a part of the gang, you must play your part.

Gang! That word again! I never wanted to be part of a gang! That life was behind me, I had moved on!

I was about to reply, telling Blofeld's_Cat exactly where he could stick his gang, but then I noticed that I had a new private message. BondBabe2000! I'd forgotten about her with all this Polly business!

Hi hun. im worried about u. y r u not going 2 see DAD? this is not like u.

What should I say? I couldn't tell her about Polly! Then another message arrived:

hu are u going 2 see scooby doo with? plz tell me ur not going wiv anuva woman.

Without thinking, I replied:

Stop crowding me! You're such a nag! I need some space!

I closed the browser, pressed start, selected *Turn off your computer*, waited until the message popped up saying *It is now safe to turn off your computer* and furiously switched it off.

I couldn't stay angry for long. The next day was *Scooby–Doo* day. There was a palpable sense of tension at school. Word had got round about the date, and now the whole of Year Six was coming.

By the evening, we were all descending upon Kingswood Shopping Centre in groups of four, each driven by someone's mum or dad. Thomas's mum drove us (my mum was picking us up). Throughout the journey, Thomas kept whispering, 'Are you gonna kiss her? Are you gonna kiss her?'

Most of Year Six were already outside the cinema.

'Where is she? Can you see her? Are you gonna kiss her?'

We got out of the car, and the crowd parted to reveal Polly and her friends, standing by the entrance to the foyer.

As I walked towards her, I realised I'd never actually spoken to her before. I played it suave and simply said, 'Hey, gorgeous babe.'

We all filed into the cinema, taking up an entire row of seats with the boys on one side and the girls on the other. In the middle, joining them together, was me and Polly. Polly and me. Things started well. During the trailers I did my classic trailers joke (when the age rating for a trailer appeared which was a 'U trailer', I turned to her and said 'You trailer!', which she silently loved).

After 90 minutes, I still didn't have my arm around Polly. I knew the film was going to end soon because Scooby-Doo had just defeated the villain by sneezing on him. Should I just do it? I'd never been in this situation before, I didn't know what to do! And then suddenly, Polly whispered, 'Are you going to put your arm around me or what?'

Yes! I did the yawn move and stretched my arm towards her. I'm not sure why I did that when the arm had been invited, but Thomas had recently told me about the yawn move so it must have been on my mind.

But just before my arm settled on her shoulder, it hit me. What was I doing? I was sitting here watching *Scooby–Doo* while other people in the same building were watching *Die Another Day* on release night. And why? So I could put my arm round a girl. How could I have been so stupid? FlemingFan was right: of course I couldn't join the conversation a day late! What was I thinking? Not only that, but I was about to cheat on the love of my life. Sure, I couldn't physically put my arm around BondBabe2000, but could I talk about *Die Another Day* with Polly? I stood up.

'What are you doing?'

'Listen, Polly, what we've had today has been special, but I'm not who you think I am. You deserve better than me. I've lied to you. I'm with someone else.'

'I don't care, I don't actually fancy you anyway.'

'What? Look, I have to go.'

I looked for the nearest exit, glancing from right to left (skilfully). It was to the right, past the girls! I began to make my exit.

'Sorry… excuse me… sorry…'

I tripped and fell onto Rachel Salmon's lap. 'What you doing, get off me, you weirdo!'

'Sorry, I have to, sorry… sorry…'

Somebody on the row behind whispered, 'Excuse me, mate, you're blocking the film.'

'Good! I'm *glad* I'm blocking the film! I'm glad I'm blocking you from seeing the worst film ever made while elsewhere in this very cinema, some people are watching *Die Another Day* on release night, which among other things features the first ever hovercraft chase in a James Bond film!'

I was back in the foyer. Screens to my left and right. *Die Another Day* was playing in one of them, but which? The electric screens outside each one happened to be malfunctioning that day, which meant that the only way of finding *Die Another Day* was by dramatically bursting from screen to screen!

My Big Fat Greek Wedding. No!

The Scorpion King. No!

Ice Age. No! (And why didn't Polly choose that? It's a much better family film.)

Where was *Die Another Day*?!

Then I heard it. The familiar strains of the Bond theme. I followed the sound. Screen One! Of course! Of course it was in Screen One, the biggest screen. I kicked the door off its hinges and ran in.

It was the end credits. The film was over. People were on their feet applauding. Amidst the clapping I heard someone say, 'That is the best film I have ever seen. Particularly the hovercraft chase. If that wasn't the last showing of the day, I'd watch it again straight away.'

I sat in silence as Mum drove us home. I knew what I had to do. I had to apologise to BondBabe2000 before it was too late. I entered my login details.

USER BANNED.

Another user has reported you for inappropriate and aggressive behaviour. As result you have been banned from CommanderBond.net for life.

I had lost everything. And I was all my own fault. I knew that joining another gang would bring me nothing but trouble.

The next day in Maths class, Mrs Wigley announced,

'Settle down, settle down. Today we will be looking at polygons.'

But all I heard was *Polly gone.*

The rest of Year Six must have heard it too because they all started laughing and chanting *Polly Gone, Polly Gone* and throwing rulers and protractors at me. Polly threw a scented gel pen at me. Mrs Wigley even joined in – she threw a pair of compasses at me and said, 'I think he got the point.'

In that moment, I vowed never, ever (for definite this time) to join another gang. And I also made another vow. A secondary vow. And that was never, ever, to get close to another woman. After everything that had happened with Sally Strawberry, Polly and BondBabe2000, I knew it could only ever end in one thing.

Pain.

i have this friend and i hate him
i hate him because every time we go to wetherspoons
he looks at the menu and says
oh look, beer & burger's on

everyone knows that beer and burger is always on
it's a permanent fixture
it's part of the menu.
it's almost like he does it on *purpose*
because he *knows* it pisses me off

Through the Tears

I asked the barman if he accepted cards and, if so, whether there was a minimum. There was no minimum. But there was a fifty pence charge for all transactions. I began to cry. And through the tears, I could just make out that the barman was also crying. Perhaps my own tears had set him off. Or perhaps, deep down, he knew that the charge was both arbitrary and unnecessary.

i applied to appear on love island
thinking it was called love ireland
now i'm stuck in majorca
everyone's shagging each other
and there's no guinness

Advent

Fifteen days into December, I realised that I had forgotten to buy an advent calendar. I quickly bought one and took it home to catch up on the doors I had missed. In the frenzy, I accidentally opened and ate December 25th instead of 15th. I had no choice but to put a turkey in the oven, pull some crackers and watch *Love Actually*. Ten days later, my family couldn't understand why I was being so difficult, but I just couldn't bring myself to watch *Love Actually* twice in ten days.

A Short Play about What the Dentist Can't Bloody Stand

[The DENTIST is finishing a PATIENT's filling]

DENTIST: All done.

[The PATIENT leaves. The DENTIST turns to the audience]

DENTIST: Do you know what I can't bloody stand? When the age ratings on the spines of DVD boxes don't line up. Especially if it's a trilogy and the age ratings on two of them line up but one is slightly lower or higher. It looks awful on the shelf and I can't bloody stand it.

[Curtain]

Suspicion

Shortly after I entered the station, a voice told me to report anyone acting suspiciously. I went straight to the information desk and told the assistant about my girlfriend, that she no longer tells me she loves me, she suddenly keeps having to work late and a few days ago I received a text message thanking me for an amazing – and exhausting ;) – night, which I suspected may have been sent to the wrong person. He told me that unless she turned up at the station with a bomb, there was little he could do.

Poem for Bert (Who Pledged for a Personalised Piece in the Book but Who I Have Never Met)

Tycoon

Browsing the blurbs in the romance section of the bookshop, I noticed that all men were described as tycoons. I didn't know what this meant but it was clearly very sexy, so I decided to become one. A quick Google search led me to a piece of software, which I've been using for a few weeks. It seems to be working – as the manager of a theme park containing over five rollercoasters, I'm already feeling a lot sexier.

i've started wearing the one direction perfume
the pastel pink box caught my eye in boots
i'd only popped in for some sudafed
but i left with nine bottles of you & i
it wasn't even on offer

Mrs Busby and the Missing Television

It seemed an extraordinary coincidence that Mrs Busby's television disappeared on the same day she gave her house key to a stranger.

Mrs Busby had joined DoggyBorrow.com in January at the suggestion of her son Daryl as she was longer mobile enough to take her dog Ziggy for his morning walk. She did not receive any messages until Friday, when TV_st£@ler_ got in touch to say that he would love to take Ziggy for a walk every morning. Mrs Busby was delighted. Ziggy was already growing sluggish and she felt very guilty.

Mrs Busby arranged for TV_st£@ler_ to collect Ziggy every morning at 8am and return him at 9am. Mrs Busby would have preferred an hour earlier as Michael took her to church just before 8am, but TV_st£@ler_ insisted that 8am was all he could do. It was decided that Mrs Busby would leave the key underneath a flowerpot so TV_st£@ler_ could let himself in.

Mrs Busby noticed that the television was missing as soon as she returned from church. She couldn't help but wonder whether TV_st£@ler_ had anything to do with it and did, for the briefest of moments, consider sending him a message. She thought better of it, though. TV_st£@ler_ was doing her a tremendous favour and she would hate to cause offence. A moment later, her son Daryl arrived carrying a new flat-screen television.

Thought you'd enjoy watching *Downton* on something a bit bigger, he said.

Mrs Busby was delighted. She was also delighted to notice over the next week or so that, thanks to TV_st£@ler_, Ziggy was already beginning to seem a lot happier and healthier.

Montage

My favourite part of any reality TV show is the best bits montage which plays when a contestant is eliminated. I decided that it would be good to have my own best bits video ready for if I ever die unexpectedly, so I tried to acquire as much existing CCTV footage of myself as possible. Only Pita Hut Kebabs was willing to hand over the footage, but it was already enough to cover the length of 'Angels' by Robbie Williams. I have emailed a private YouTube link to my friends and family and told them only to watch it if the worst happens.

A Short Play about EastEnders

[The DOCTOR is sitting at his desk. There is a knock at the door]

DOCTOR: Come in.

[MARTIN enters]

MARTIN: Hello, Doctor.

DOCTOR: Hello, Martin. Please sit down. What seems to be the problem this time?

MARTIN: Well, it started last week. I watched *EastEnders* for the first time. And since then, I've had trouble sleeping.

DOCTOR: I see. What happens when you try to sleep?

MARTIN: Well, every time I close my eyes, I hear the *EastEnders* theme tune.

DOCTOR: I see. Including the opening drum beats?

MARTIN: Yes. Sometimes even when I blink, I hear the first drum beat.

DOCTOR: Right. And are there any other symptoms?

MARTIN: I don't just hear the music. I see the title sequence too.

DOCTOR: Is it the original or the post-2000 version featuring the Millennium Dome?

MARTIN: I think the Dome is there, yes.

DOCTOR: I see. Have you kept your eyes closed long enough to see what happens after the title sequence?

MARTIN: Yes.

DOCTOR: And?

MARTIN: The episode begins.

DOCTOR: Is it a particular episode?

MARTIN: No, it's different every time. Last night I watched Dirty Den present Angie with the divorce papers.

DOCTOR: Happy Christmas, Angie.

MARTIN: That's right.

DOCTOR: Right. Well, I'm afraid I don't know what to suggest.

MARTIN: Right.

[Curtain]

Still

To try and feel famous for a day, I hired an actor to point and stare while I stood completely still in Madame Tussauds. I arrived as soon as the doors opened and placed myself next to George Clooney. My actor arrived ten minutes later. People noticed us and some even photographed me. After a few hours, one visitor asked the actor who I was. I suddenly realised that we hadn't covered this scenario in the workshops. He panicked and said I was Ryan Gosling. I stood in silence for the next forty minutes while she and her friends discussed how much better my body and face look in my films.

find a job you love
and you'll never work a day
until you stop loving it
because it's your job

Instapoet

In an attempt to emulate the success of many notable Instagram poets, I wrote a three-line epigram eulogising the beauty and intelligence of an unnamed lover, while sorrowfully lamenting the demise of our relationship. As soon as it was published, my girlfriend demanded to know who it was about. I explained that the woman was fictional, I was trying out a new style. She laughed at me then asked why I had drawn a spoon next to it. I explained that it was supposed to be a wilting flower. She laughed at me some more then told me to go and get a pie out of the freezer.

Christmas

I wish it could be Christmas every day. I love the crackers, the dinner, the hat, scarf, gloves and togetherness. I like January too. I still wear my hat, scarf, gloves and smile. In February, I still feel good, still wear my hat and scarf and gloves, still smile. I still wear the hat and scarf and gloves in March, but the smile starts to fade. By April, it's gone. Things start to annoy me in May. Little things like being given the wrong change or warm weather or people wearing shorts or T-shirts or both. In June, I get aggressive. I get tanked up on mulled wine, throw Christingles through shop windows and post Christmas puddings through people's letterboxes. On the first day of July, I go to the park in my hat, scarf and gloves, looking for topless sunbathers to throw baubles at, hit with crackers, smear with bread sauce and cover up with wrapping paper. I'm often in court by mid-July (which I enjoy because the judge looks like Santa). I usually get released in October, just as the days are getting darker. I roam the streets alone, listening, waiting. And then, one day, I hear it. Usually in Marks and Spencer's or John Lewis. Wizzard. And the smile starts to creep back. Not long now.

A Short Play about a Rebel without a Cause and His Young Conquest

[A REBEL WITHOUT A CAUSE has taken his YOUNG CON-QUEST for a ride in his new sports car]

YOUNG CONQUEST: The speed of this vehicle is very exciting.

[Curtain]

Life is like a box of chocolates.
You never know what you're gonna get.

[But you can probably work it out. If the information card is missing, try smelling the chocolates. Also, look for visual clues; white chocolate is often lighter in colour than milk or dark chocolate. I'm not promising that you won't encounter an unwelcome nut or an unexpectedly hard toffee. All I'm saying is that, in life (and in chocolate), deploying a little common sense rather than going in blind could reduce the possibility of an unpleasant surprise, such as accidentally eating a coffee-flavoured one.]

Quip

I wanted to take a beer into a theatre show so I asked the barman if he had any plastics. He asked what on earth I meant by 'plastics' and I explained that I was looking for a plastic glass. He told me that this was a theatre, not a student bar, of course he did not have any 'plastics'. He then asked for ten pounds so I held up my card and said do you take plastic? I thought it was a wonderful quip but he didn't laugh. During the interval, I wrote down what had happened and added it to my book manuscript, in the hope that the quip would one day gain some recognition.

The Headmaster's Address

HEADMASTER: This is not a good school.

[The pupils gasp]

HEADMASTER: This is an excellent school.

[The pupils are relieved]

[Curtain]

Quip 2

We were asked to place all bags in the overhead locker as our row was next to the emergency exit. The lady by the exit asked if her coat could remain on her lap. No, the flight attendant said, but she could wear it. Fumbling into her coat, she bemoaned the high temperature inside the aircraft. Quick as a flash, I turned to the lady and said that if she got too hot during the flight, she could always open the door. I thought it was a wonderful quip but she didn't laugh. During taxiing, I wrote down what had happened and added it to my book manuscript, in the hope that the quip would one day gain some recognition.

Yoda

Walking through Trafalgar Square one afternoon, I passed a man dressed as Yoda who appeared to be sitting in mid-air. Even more extraordinary was the fact that nobody seemed to find this extraordinary. He was sitting in mid-air and people were just walking by as if it was the most normal thing in the world.

I put down my bag and stared at him for half an hour, trying to work out how he was doing it. There was nothing beneath him; no transparent stilts, no perspex support. Nothing. Just a man dressed as Yoda, holding a long staff and sitting in mid-air.

I shouted up to him,

How are you doing that?

No response.

Excuse me, how are you doing that?

Yoda, I am.

Don't be silly, I said, That's just a costume. How are you sitting in mid-air?

No response.

I stared up at him for another hour. It was getting late and the crowds were starting to thin. But I wasn't going anywhere, not until I'd seen Yoda return to the ground.

As the sky grew darker, he began glancing down every few minutes to check if I was still there. I was.

Eventually, he spoke again:

Will you go away please?

No.

Please go away, I need to go home now.

Go on then.

I can't if you're here.

Why not?

Because I don't like people to see me get down.

Why not?

139

It spoils the illusion.

I looked down. The man didn't want me to know how he was doing it. So why should I? I picked up my bag and turned to leave, taking one last look up at him. He was literally floating in mid-air! I threw down my bag.

I'm not going anywhere, mate.

Go away! He was half shouting now. I need the toilet.

You're just going to have to come down then.

He clenched his fist around the staff. I sat down, took a banana from my bag and continued watching him.

Quip 3

I received a text message from someone lined up to perform at my new poetry night, explaining that his wife was due to give birth any day soon so he might have to suddenly pull out. I immediately replied: *If only you'd done that 9 months ago!!!!* He didn't reply, and I later heard that he had found the message distasteful. I wrote down what had happened and added it to my book manuscript, in the hope that the quip would one day gain some recognition.

if you can't handle me at my worst
then you sure as hell don't deserve
to feel that you have to

if i'm at my worst
just say *i can't handle this*
i won't be offended
my worst *is* annoying

i thought you were the one

but then you got excited about a massage chair at the airport

so i had to let you go

(i just can't be with someone who doesn't find those things weird)

Easy Come, Easy Go

I was online, browsing a shopping website,
just killing some time before turning in for the night.

But I kept seeing these passionate five star reviews
by someone called Steve_1962.

He'd reviewed a printer, a scanner, a pink mini fridge,
a thousand-piece jigsaw of the Golden Gate Bridge,

a multi-pack of miniature handheld food blenders,
a pair of industrial ear defenders,

a packet of sixty-six scented gel pens,
a boxed set of every single series of *Friends* (on VHS),

some lipstick, a Pritt Stick, a box of forty selfie sticks,
a thousand-page book about the rise of the Bolsheviks.

Anyway, I don't know it happened, I got carried away,
I was tired.

I ordered the lot and it's all just arrived.

Tommy

Tommy was at home eating his dinner. It was a cold December evening and the first snow in years had fallen the night before. Tommy couldn't wait to play in it. He scoffed up his Turkey Twizzlers and ran for the front door.

Careful, Tommy! shouted his father. There's a lot of lying snow out there!

Tommy didn't listen. Within seconds, he was out in the snow. It was wonderful. He ran up and down the garden, throwing snowballs through the open window at his mother and father. Before long, he was exhausted. He lay on his back in the snow. Then he heard a voice.

I've got a quad bike.

Tommy sat up. Who said that?

I've got a quad bike.

There it was again! It seemed to be coming from the ground. Tommy placed his ear to the snowy grass.

I've got a quad bike.

Tommy realised it was the snow that was talking. So *that's* what his father had meant by lying snow. Tommy knew it was impossible for snow to own a quad bike.

Gun

I could never understand why a certain country refused to ban its guns until I read about the fantasy of being the Good Guy with a Gun during an incident. I could see why this was an appealing idea and I decided to become that person. Real guns are illegal here, so instead I became the Good Guy with a Glue Gun. I haven't saved any lives yet but the local community now know that whenever I'm around (and there's a plug socket nearby), they're safe – and that's enough for me.

like yoda i started speaking
intelligent and wise, i wanted to sound
stuck like this, i now am
to hang out with me any more, no one wants
blame them, i do not
annoying myself, i am
funny any more, it is not

Bible

In an attempt to make some money, I rewrote the Bible. Jesus's miracles included posting a 25-second Instagram Story and writing a 300-character tweet. His blue badge was removed after some unsavoury early tweets were uncovered but it reappeared three days later, much to the amazement of his twelve followers. The book was commercially unsuccessful and critics dismissed the plot as unrealistic.

she asked me
if i'm ever naughty

i leant forward
and whispered

sometimes
instead of retyping my password
i just copy and paste it

Accident

A woman called to ask whether I had been involved with an accident that wasn't my fault. The signal was poor so I moved to the window and fell out of it. Lying broken limbed in the back yard, I told her what had happened and thus began a long and meandering debate over who was to blame. I argued that I would not have fallen had she not called, while she cited Aristotelian theories of culpability and free will to suggest that the fall was my choice. I conceded defeat and then dialled for an ambulance, but the battery died before the call could connect.

Frequent Flyer

I'm somebody who flies a lot, so I thought it would be a good exercise for me to write about flying. I suppose it's fair to say I'm always on Airplane Mode (!). When something becomes second nature, you often forget to truly notice and observe what you're actually doing. So this is more for my benefit than yours, but it will at least give those of you with fairly basic, ground-based lives an insight into that of a frequent flyer.

***

My journey begins with the bit we all hate: packing. Fortunately, I'm well used to packing by now so these days I leave it until just six days before travelling.

With my luggage in tow, I stroll breezily into the terminal, casually glancing at my printed and laminated email confirmation for the check-in details. Then, with a calm air of grace, I head towards security.

As the security guard asks me to place my items into a tray, I quip that security can never be too careful these days, I could have a gun! I then calmly saunter through the X-ray, my heart rate quickening in relaxation.

My belongings are returned to me and I head towards Departures. As a frequent flyer, I know that it's important to head to the departure gate as soon as possible – you never know when a plane might leave early.

Before long, we all file onto the plane and the flight attendants pass through the cabin to check that all seatbelts are fastened. I catch the eye of one and casually enquire about the pilot's flying experience. She tells me there's no need to be scared and I quip, I'm not scared, winking at her (with both eyes).

As the plane begins to pick up speed on the runway, I clench the armrests and close my eyes in a deeply meditative manner. The lady next to me tells me that you're more likely to be struck by lightning than killed in a plane crash, and I calmly ask why she's talking about dying just before we take off.

Even for someone who flies as often as I do, there's nothing quite like the moment of take-off and, as the plane leaves the ground, I smile to myself and vomit into the sick bag. We encounter some turbulence on the way up and I let out a sophisticated scream. A pretty flight attendant walks over.

Sir, I need to ask you to relax, she says, her voice loaded with sexual chemistry. I look up at her and, with the faintest hint of a seductive smile, demand to be let off the plane.

Sir, I can't let you off the plane, she purrs back at me, we're 35,000 feet above the ground. I demand to speak to the pilot.

The pilot can't speak to you because he is flying the plane, she replies, and I quip that he clearly isn't a very good pilot if he can't multitask. She calls over another flight attendant, presumably to share the quip with him. He hands me a red piece of paper titled *On-board Warning Card*. It reads:

Your behaviour on this flight is causing discomfort to other passengers. Any further disturbance may result in the pilot landing the plane at the nearest possible airport and your arrest.

I casually glance out of the window and begin to cry. The lady next to me squeezes my hand and I vomit in her face. The attractive flight attendant returns and, as a fun and flirty move, I jump out of my seat, shove her out of the way and run down the aisle to the cockpit, banging on the door and begging to be let off the plane.

Three more flight attendants approach and a fight ensues. Although clearly the strongest and most skilled in combat, I allow them to overpower me and keep me pinned to the ground for the next forty minutes.

The pilot announces that we will be making an unscheduled landing at Humberside Airport to remove a passenger. The other passengers groan and shout and jokingly call me things like dickhead, bellend, idiot and twat.

I remain pinned to the ground until we land and I am removed from the plane by four armed police officers. After six hours of intense questioning, an initial hearing date is set, and I am released on bail – just in time for my business meeting in Hull.

Parky

Sarah's husband loved Michael Parkinson. *Parky*, he called him. Sarah found Parky boring. She went online and found a website full of people who also found Parky boring. She met her new husband there. The wedding had a *Parky is Boring* theme.

i thought you were the one

but then you used a mouse with your laptop in a cafe

so i had to let you go

Streak

One of my greatest peeves in life is when the food arrives at a restaurant and somebody else's meal looks better than mine. I'm an emotional person and I'm not very good at hiding my disappointment. My girlfriend got very angry with me for making a scene in Pizza Express last week. But to be fair, my Sloppy Giuseppe did shit all over her Margherita; on this occasion she was a loser and, with it being the third (!) time in a row that I had won, it felt appropriate to scream the phrase *killing streak*.

Boarding

In a rare moment of extravagance while booking a flight online, I opted for Speedy Boarding. I boarded with two old men who immediately began making suggestive comments to a flight attendant. I confronted them and the captain was forced to intervene. It turned out that I had accidentally joined the wrong queue. I was asked to leave the aircraft or pay an extra £30 to upgrade to Seedy Boarding.

Not all those who wander are lost.

[But some are. If you spot someone frantically refreshing Google Maps and just, you know, generally looking lost, then for God's sake offer them some directions. Look, don't get me wrong, I love a wander as much as the next guy. I'm all for putting my headphones on, loading up some Bon Iver and going for a long walk. But I'll be the first to admit when a wander has turned into lostness. Put it this way; if I've wandered halfway up a mountain and it starts to get cold and dark, then I'm not ashamed to call Mountain Rescue.]

Gymnasium

I decided, out of curiosity, to visit a gymnasium. Inside, I discovered labourers groaning in despair as they struggled to lift various objects or maintain their position atop ceaseless, mechanised hulks. Instinctively inclined to help those in distress, I rushed from person to person, sharing the load of an object, lifting them to their feet or disconnecting the power from their machine. One of their tormentors, a muscular, well-oiled man, ordered to me to leave the premises lest he call the authorities. Leave I did, but not before vowing to expose these barbaric, oppressive, unhealthy conditions.

if you're hungry, have an apple
if you're thirsty, have a glass of water
if you're cold, put a jumper on
if you're bored, go for a run

(This piece is dedicated to my dad.)

Feels

A friend sent me a video titled Cat Massages Another Cat and told me that it would give me *all the feels*. I was just about to click Play when I realised that the office was maybe not the best environment in which to experience every feeling simultaneously for the first time in my life. I replied honestly, explaining that, although curious, I had never done anything like this before and would prefer to try it in a comfortable and controlled setting with someone like him present, just in case. He's coming over tonight. We're just going to chill out, drink a few beers and then maybe see if I fancy it, no pressure.

Ecstasy

*Since I began performing spoken word, I've seen many poets reading poems
about drugs. I'm not exactly Mr Drugs, but a few weeks ago, I had a bit of
an experience. The title of this poem is a clue as to what the substance was.*

***

House party
all my friends and me
the DJ drops a beat
and I drop an E

My heart starts pounding
my pupils dilate
but I'm not frowning
'cause I feel great

My friend walks past
and gives me a hug
and I'm like OH YEAH
THAT IS NICE

Then I see a girl standing
in the corner on her own
so I walk over to her
(so she's not on her own)

WHAT'S YOUR NAME?
MY NAME'S DAN.
I'VE TAKEN AN E!
WHERE YOU GOING?

She walks off
leaving me on my own
so I look for my friends
—where did they go?

Without any mates
do I look like a loser?
Nah
I'M BEST MATES WITH THE MUSIC!

Then the beat comes down
Then the beat comes down
Then the beat comes down
Then the beat comes down

And that's when I notice
yeah that's when I notice
that's when I notice
that's when I notice

my heart rate
is going pretty fast
instead of 1 – 2 – 3 – 4,
it's going 12341234

That's not normal
That's not normal
Is that normal?
That's not normal

So I go outside
and I find my mates

and I'm like 'ERE JOHN
CAN I FEEL YOUR HEART RATE?

And he's like Why?
And I'm like PLEASE
And he's like Alright
And I'm like CHEERS

JOHN, MY HEART RATE IS FASTER THAN YOURS,
YOURS IS DOING TWO PER SECOND AND MINE'S
DOING, LIKE, THREE, THAT'S NOT NORMAL,
THAT'S NOT NORMAL THAT'S NOT—

Then the beat comes up
Then the beat comes up
Then the beat comes up
Then the beat comes up

And I I I I
I I I I
I I I I
IIIII am having a panic attack!
A panic attack!
A panic attack!
A panic attack!

So John calls 999
and everyone rolls their eyes
They're like, Who's this dickhead?
What a knob

And I start crying
'cause I think I'm dying

What's that sound
It's the ambulance arriving

NEE NAR NEE NAR
NEE NEE NEE NEE
NARNARNARNARNARNAR

Then the next day
I write a poem about it

Isolation

Inspired by the origin story of Bon Iver's debut album, I booked a secluded cabin for three months on Airbnb. It would be a period of intense isolation and creativity. I would set my alarm for sunrise and spend every day writing poems and living off the land. Unfortunately, the cabin was completely unsuitable. There was no bath, no heating and no 4G for Uber Eats. I left after just two days, during which I wrote one poem. It was a moving ode to my alarm clock called 'You Wake Me Up' (although I discarded it a few days later when my mother pointed out how similar it was to 'You Raise Me Up' by Westlife).

Drop

I decided to try talking like a hip-hop artist or DJ. Instead of doing or saying things, I now dropped them. Anecdotes and jokes were not told; they dropped. Dinner was not served at six; six was when dinner dropped. I thought it sounded cool but, after a few days, my girlfriend told me to drop it.

i thought you were the one

but then you saw yourself appear on the screen at a festival and started waving, except you waved at the screen so to everyone else watching the screen, you were just waving into the distance

so i had to let you go

Serious Poem

All I really want to do
is write a serious poem
A sad poem
A poem that makes people think
He's had a bad time
I'm glad I'm not him

I want to write a poem
that I can't read without crying
and without making others cry
and approach me afterwards and say
You alright?
Can I get you a drink?
It's on me

I want to write a poem
that makes all the other poets in the room think
That's what I was trying to do

I want to write a poem
that makes anyone in the room who has been thinking of giving
poetry a go think
I'm not ready yet

I want to write a poem
that changes the atmosphere in the room
And I want that change to be noticed
by any potential promoters
who might approach me after the show

and say
It's about time you got paid for this

Manifesto

Extract from 'Daniel Piper's Day Off' (2017)

I'm going to delete Facebook. And Twitter. And Instagram. I'm going to start listening to podcasts. Reading books. Not Kindle books, I'm selling that. Books that you can feel and smell and touch and taste and read. I'm going to get rid of my iPhone. I don't need a smartphone. I don't need a phone at all. If someone needs to get in touch with me they can come and find me. I'm going to unsubscribe from all the mailing lists I'm on. I'm going to start going to galleries and exhibitions. I'm going to get a Tate Card. Join the BFI, watch old films. Get into photography, film photography. Less digital, more analogue. I'm going to get healthy. Go vegetarian. Vegan. Polio. Whatever that one is where you eat grass. Throw out all the clothes I don't wear, have a capsule wardrobe. Get a folding bike. Do a hundred press-ups every morning. Less flat whites, more filters. Less beer, more Becks Blue. I'm going to get up earlier. I'm going to be like that Army advert that says they do more before 9am than most people in a day, except I'm going to get more done before 8, I'm going to show them. I'm going to be like all those famous people who famously got up early, like Mozart. I'm going to get up, get in the shower, get showered, get in the kitchen, have some porridge, get outside and start living each day like it's my last.

I need to just get out that door and start doing the things I've always wanted to do. Like smiling at people. I've always wanted to be the kind of person who smiles at people but I never do it because I'm worried they won't smile back, and that I have a stupid smile. There's another thing: from now on I'm going to be less self-conscious about things like my smile or my clothes or how much I've read or what music I listen to. I used to love Keane. But I never felt like I could listen to them after I was talking to a girl I fancied on MSN and she asked what I was up to and I said *Just chilling out and listen-*

ing to some Keane, and she told everyone at school and my nickname became *Keane Bean,* then *Clean Bean,* then *Clean Bean from the Washing Machine,* then on a school trip to Berlin it became *Saubere Bohne aus der Waschmaschine.* I stopped listening to Keane after that, and that was when they only had one album out. There's a whole world of Keane out there that I haven't even heard. The first thing I'm going to do today is get out the door, put my headphones on and catch up on Keane.

I need to start learning to do stuff. There's so much stuff I can't do. Smiling's one of them. I can't light the hob with a lighter. I have to get someone else to do it because I'm scared. Cooking's another. Can't cook, won't cook. Don't cook, doesn't cook. Should cook. Forward rolls. I can't do them. I'm going to get out that door and start learning and doing. Today is the first day of the rest of my days.

But I'm always saying this, aren't I? Every time I go on holiday I say *When I get back I'm going to spend more time on myself and get healthier and cut my working week down to three days and cook more and do more forward rolls.* I say that kind of thing every weekend, then by Tuesday night I'm in bed eating Milkybar yoghurts and scheduling the tweets I didn't do at work because I spent all day watching conspiracy videos on YouTube about how the moon is fake. Well, no more fake moon videos. No more Milkybar yoghurts in bed. No more tweets. Just me, outside. living my life.

But how's this any different from all the other epiphanies I've had about sorting my life out? How's it different from when I spent two days in the Lake District in May and decided I was going to become a dairy farmer? Or last New Year when I was feeling a fat so I decided I was going to become Michael Phelps by buying a Fitbit? Or last week when I was feeling like I'd spent too long on Facebook and I needed to disconnect and go back to a simpler, more primitive way of life so I pre-ordered the new remake of the Nokia 3310? One thing I *am* good at is convincing myself that, in order to sort my life out, I need to buy stuff. *I'm not very happy in my job – I need a new spring/summer jacket. I haven't been eating very healthily lately – I need a new phone case. I have this dull feeling of unease and dissatisfaction, like I haven't achieved everything I should have achieved by now and I've noticed that I'm compar-*

ing myself a lot to other people at the moment – I need some posh lip balm. God knows how many times I've decided that a new app is going to sort my life out. I've got a folder on my phone called *Lifestyle*. Never use it. *Mindspace Meditation.* I used it once. It stressed me out. She was trying to make me imagine all of the aches and pains in my body melting away and she said *Start with the crown of the head*, but I didn't know which part of the head was the crown so I guessed and focused on the back of my head, then she said *Now focus on the back of your head*, and I ended up punching a wall. *MyFitnessPal.* I went through a phase of thinking I should track my calories, but stopped using it when I realised the in-built list of foods didn't include Milky-bar yoghurts and I couldn't be bothered to add them manually.

It's going to be different this time. I need to actually make changes, not just download an app or buy a coat. I need to do something to draw a line underneath all that, start afresh. I need to do something big. Something that draws a line under everything so I don't just slip back into doing nothing. Something thrilling like... like going out and finding a vending machine and... just... buying everything in it! With no clothes on!

New Year's Eve

Sitting alone at my writing desk at one minute to New Year's Day, I wished aloud that this year had never happened. A small genie appeared on my desk and asked for clarification. Do you wish that we could go back and redo this year, or that time would skip from last year to next year? he asked. The latter has never been done before so it may be wiser to select the former. Heeding his advice, I asked if we could begin this year all over again. Okay, what would you like me to change about this year? he asked. Bear in mind that there are now only twenty seconds until midnight so time is of the essence. Realising that twenty seconds would not give me enough time to ask the genie to reverse all of the terrible news stories and events of this year, I told him to forget about it, let's just carry on as normal and go straight to next year. As you wish, the genie said. Hang on, wait, I shouted as he began to fade away. Let's do this year all over again, except this time, I get invited to a New Year's Eve party. He was gone. I didn't know whether he had heard me. The sound of fireworks suddenly filled the air outside. I checked the date on my laptop. January 1st, next year.

Patrons

Ludvig Aarflot
Jacob Andrews
Helen Anslow
Kate Applebaum
Peter Archer
Lauren Archer
Jamie Ash
Sian Astor-Lewis
Athos Athanasiou
Aidan Baker
Erin Bolens
Ben Bolton
Connor Boshuijer
Felicity Bown
Nicholas Browne
Carl Burkitt
Immi Calderwood
Emily Clay
Will Clay
Rachel Cobb
Roberta Colombano
Kyle Cooper
Alice Crawley-Carr
Saucy-Jack Crikey
Daisy Crooke
Hannah Crossan-Smith
Jen Cunliffe
Tom Dale
Melissa Davies
Paul Davis
Eamonn Dawe
Sue Dawes

Gareth Dawson
Alex Day
Julia De Groot
Becky Dennis
Sarah Dullaghan
Jenny Dunn
Amy Eade
Laurie Eaves
Laura Elliott
Gareth Fairlie
Sarah Faulkner
Maria Ferguson
Paul Flatt
Flävia
David Forrest
Angela Foster
Max Fulham
Alexa Garner
Anna Gilbert
Chris Gilleard
Adam Gilleard
Mike Gorman (Improv Killed My Dog)
Jemima Foxtrot and Ed Hadfield
Marti Hall
Nichola Hardy
Simon Harper
Cat Hepburn
Simon Hill
Rebecca Hindle
Sara Hirsch
Becky Hirst
Jane Hogan
James Holden
Dom Hornsby
Matthew Hunter
Alex Insch

Sebastian Jaskiewicz
Deremyre John
Kathryn Joseph
Leyla Josephine
Victor Kanopelko
Brodie Kershaw
Evelina Kvartūnaitė
Hannah Leslie
Ewa Less Man
Danny Lunn
Pam Lyon
Clare MacGregor
Max Machen
Rachel Marsh
Ann Marshall
Carmina Masoliver
Hakuna Matata
Ben Meagher
Alexandre Mecattaf
Doug Menzies
Josh Meredith
Joren Merkus
Ian A Millington
Rebecca Mitchell
Vikki Mizon
Adam Moore
Josh Morter
Mas Moyo
Sharina Muller
Ryan Mulrooney
Camilla Murray
Carlo Navato
Rowen Nicola
Joh Nuh
Bednarz O'Connell
Joseph O'Tweefe

Selina Ocean
Jesse Oomen
Jonathan Gentle & Marilena Parouti
Sandra Pham
James Piper
JE Pourcho
Rosie Preston
Rachael Procter
Happily Quin
Ronan Radin
Eleanor Richards
Annemieke Riepma
Tony Roberts
Andrew Rowe
Sam Small
Rik Sprenkels
Cole Stacey
Wendy Steatham
Sydnie Storm
Kate Thorogood
Val Thorrington
Diane Tingley
James Tomkins
Cat Turhan
Andrew Turner
Guntars Ūpis
Pim van der Mijl
Thomas Wade
Stug Dave Waitrose
Sinéad Wall
Kyrah Werner
Sara Weston
Michaela Wheater
Rachel Williams
Sam Woolard

Anna Yule
Jelle Zwart

Acknowledgements

Thank you to the team at Unbound for not considering my writing too arbitrary and unnecessary to publish.

Thank you to my Instagram followers for the little dopamine hits.

Thank you to anybody who has ever booked me for a gig (particularly those who have offered drink vouchers). Special thanks to Michael at The Poetry Takeaway, and to all at Underbelly.

Thank you to everybody I have met within the world of performance who has offered inspiration, encouragement or a useful email address; Gecko, Maria and Jack to name a few.

Thank you to everyone at Rhymes With Orange for the frittata, the constant support, and for welcoming me into the coolest (and, ironically, warmest) poetry gang in town. Special thanks to the Nelsons for your generosity in the form of book patronage, chocolates and macaroons.

Thank you to Rebecca for your generosity, stuffed partridge and ceaseless supply of Third Generation Chardonnay.

Thank you to Deborah and everyone at the wonderful Year Out Drama.

Thank you to all my friends. You're both great. Only joking; thanks to Paul and John and to the rest of my many, many friends. You know who you are (could you let me know?).

Thank you Mum and Dad for everything you have ever provided for me, not least the wonderful upbringing. (Unrelated: please don't forget that you owe me a pair of Dr Martens as a replacement for the ones you lost during the house move.)

Thank you James for always being a brother and a best friend to look up to.

Finally, thank you Jemima for supporting, tolerating and [to make happy]ing me for almost a decade. As I said in 2009: I like you.